GW01003659

It's another Quality Book from CGP

This book is for anyone studying <u>Graphic Products</u> at GCSE.

Let's face it, D&T is pretty hard-going — you've got a whole load of technical stuff to learn on top of doing your project.

Happily this CGP book helps to take the headache out of all that learning. We've explained all the technical stuff — and drawn plenty of pictures to make the whole thing that bit clearer. Plus we've stuck in some handy hints to help make your project a winner.

And in true CGP-style it's got some daft bits in to try and make the whole experience at least vaguely entertaining for you.

What CGP is all about

Our sole aim here at CGP is to produce the highest quality books — carefully written, immaculately presented and dangerously close to being funny.

Then we work our socks off to get them out to you — at the cheapest possible prices.

Contents

Published by Coordination Group Publications Ltd.

Contributors:
Juliet Cash
Martin Chester
Stephen Guinness
Gemma Hallam
Kerry Kolbe
Simon Little
Tim Major
Alan Nanson
Andy Park
Julie Schofield
Karen Steel
Claire Thompson
Anthony Wilcock

ISBN: 1-84146-791-X

With thanks to Juliet Cash, Dominic Hall, Alan Nanson, Glenn Rogers,
Angela Ryder, Karen Steel and Anthony Wilcock for the proofreading.

Groovy website: www.cgpbooks.co.uk

Jolly bits of clipart from CorelDRAW
With thanks to TECHSOFT UK Ltd for permission to use a screenshot from *Techsoft Design Tools — 2D Desig*
and to PTC for permission to use a screenshot from *Pro/Desktop*

Printed by Elanders Hindson, Newcastle upon Tyne.

Text, design, layout and original illustrations © Coordination Group Publications Ltd. 2002
All rights reserved.

Design Brief

The process of designing and making something is called 'the design process' (gosh). The whole process can take a while — so, like many pineapples, it's usually broken down into smaller chunks.

The Design Process is Similar in Industry and School

It's no accident that the things you'll have to do for your Design and Technology project are pretty similar to what happens in industry.

- The best products are those that address a real need.
- That's why companies spend so much time and money on customer research. The more people there are who would actually use a product, the more chance it stands of being a roaring success.
- The best ideas for Design and Technology projects are also those that meet a genuine need.

The rest of this section describes a typical design process.

It shows the sort of thing that happens in industry every day.

It also shows the stages you need to go through while you're putting a Design and Technology project together.

First get your Idea for a New Product

First things first... whether you're working in the research and development department of a multinational company, or you're putting together your project, you need to explain why a new product is needed.

It could be for one of the following reasons:

1) There are problems with an existing product.
2) The performance of an existing design could be improved.
3) There's a gap in the market that you want to fill.

The Design Brief explains Why your Product is Needed

The design brief explains why there might be a need for a new product.
It should include the following:

1) an outline of the problem and who it affects
2) the need arising from the problem
3) what you intend to do about it (e.g. design and make...)
4) how your product will be used
5) the environment it will be used in

DESIGN BRIEF FOR: BACKSCRATCHER / TURNIP HOLDER

No currently commercially available backscratcher has an in-built capacity for turnip storage.

So we will manufacture a product to meet this need for those people having itchy backs and modest turnip storage requirements (up to 4 turnips).

Basically, the design brief should concentrate on the problem you're trying to solve.

Remember — your project doesn't have to involve turnips...

Your design brief should be simple and concise, and allow you room for development. A design brief should not be a detailed description of what you intend to make — you can only say this after you've designed it and tried stuff out. Got that... describe the problem first. The rest comes later.

Research

Once you've written your design brief, you can start <u>researching</u> your project.
This is what life is all about.

Research can help you get Ideas

It's worth doing your research <u>carefully</u> — it can give you
loads of <u>ideas</u> for the rest of the design process.
The point of doing research is to:

1) check that people will actually <u>want</u> your product
   (although you might have done this already when you
   <u>chose</u> your project).

2) find out what makes an existing product <u>good</u> or <u>bad</u> —
   talk to people who actually use this kind of product,
   and see what they like or dislike.

3) find out the <u>materials</u>, pre-manufactured <u>components</u>, <u>techniques</u> and <u>ingredients</u>
   that you can use, and how they will affect the manufacturing and selling <u>costs</u>.

4) give you a good starting point for <u>designing</u>.

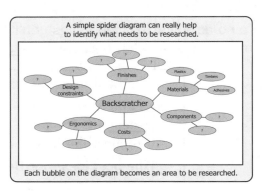

A simple spider diagram can really help
to identify what needs to be researched.

Each bubble on the diagram becomes an area to be researched.

There are Different Kinds of Research

You can do <u>different kinds</u> of research. This might include:

1) Questionnaires — to find out people's likes/dislikes and so on. This will help you identify
   your <u>target group</u> and find out <u>market trends</u> (e.g. what things are becoming more <u>popular</u>).

2) Disassembling a product (i.e. taking it apart) — this will help you
   find out how a current product is <u>made</u> and how it <u>works</u>. It could
   also give you information about different <u>materials</u> and <u>processes</u>
   used, and how <u>existing</u> products meet potential users' needs.

3) Measuring — to find out the <u>weights</u> and <u>sizes</u> of current products.
   This might give you an idea of the possible size, shape and weight of
   <u>your</u> product. You could also do some kind of <u>sensory analysis</u>
   (e.g. you could see how it tastes, feels, looks and smells).

Research Analysis means Drawing Conclusions

Once you've done your research, you'll need to come to some <u>conclusions</u>. This means deciding
how to use the information to help you with your design. This is called <u>research analysis</u>.

Try to do the following:

1) <u>Pick out</u> the useful information.

2) <u>Explain</u> what impact the research will have on your designs.

3) <u>Suggest</u> ways forward from the research gathered.

By the time you've done all this, you should have some ideas about how to tackle your project.

I disassembled my dog — he doesn't work any more...

Research is important. Trust me. More important at this stage than cutting wood or moulding
plastic. And one more thing while I'm ranting... you could also spend some time doing 'book
research', e.g. finding out about any British or European standards your product will have to meet.

Design Specification

Once you've picked out the main points of your research, you're ready to put together a design specification. So put that chisel away... you're not ready to do anything practical yet.

The Design Specification is a List of Conditions to Meet

The design specification describes the restrictions and possibilities of the product.
It's a good point to start from when you get round to doing the more creative stuff.

1) The design specification gives certain conditions that the product will have to meet. Try to put your specification together in bullet form as specific points, rather than a paragraph of explanations.

> E.g. if your research tells you that people would never buy a backscratcher weighing 300 grams or more, then your design specification might include the statement, "Must weigh less than 300 grams."

2) Once you've come up with a design, you need to compare it to the specification and confirm that each point is satisfied.

    E.g. If your design specification contains these two points, then all of your designs should be at least 400 mm long and have a variety of colours.

> "The minimum length will be 400 mm."
> "The product should be multicoloured."

3) Some points might be harder to compare to your specification simply by looking at the product.

> E.g. "The product should feel comfortable."

    For this, you'll need to get someone to test the product once it's been made/modelled.

4) Include points to describe some or all of the following:
    - a description of how it should look
    - details about what it has to do/be
    - materials, ingredients and joining methods
    - details of size/weight
    - safety points to consider
    - financial constraints

You might need to make More than One Specification

You'll probably need to produce several specifications as your project develops:

> Initial Design Specification — this is your first design specification. It should be done after your research analysis.

1) As you develop your design, you'll probably want to make some changes to your design specification. This is fine, as long as your design brief is being met and you have taken your research analysis into account.

2) Maybe as a result of some of your modelling (see page 5) you'll find that certain materials aren't suitable. You can add this information to an updated specification.

3) You can keep doing this until you end up with a final product specification.

I'd never buy a backscratcher that didn't glow in the dark...

If I told you that design specifications were going to get your pulse racing, you'd probably suspect I was lying. And of course, I would be lying. To be honest, they're a bit dull. But making a design specification is a vital step in designing and manufacturing a new product. So learn about it.

Generating Proposals

Now hold on to your hats, my wild young things — this is where it all starts to get a bit more interesting. This is the creative bit. This is where you start generating ideas.

There are a few Tricks that can help you Get Started

The following are suggestions to help you get started with designing:

1) Create a mood board — this is a load of different images, words, materials, colours and so on that might trigger ideas for your design.

2) Brainstorm — think up key words, questions and initial thoughts relating to your product. (Start off by just writing whatever ideas come into your head — analyse them later.)

3) Work from an existing product — but change some of its features or production methods so that it fits in with your specification.

4) Break the task up into smaller parts — e.g. design the 'look' of the product (aesthetics), then look at the technology involved and so on.

You need to Come up with a Range of Designs

1) You need to annotate (i.e. add notes to) your designs to fully explain your ideas. These notes could be about:

- materials
- size
- user
- shape
- cost
- advantages and disadvantages
- production method
- functions

2) You need to produce a wide range of appropriate solutions that you think could actually be made.

3) Try to use a range of techniques for presenting your designs. A good thing to do is to use different drawing techniques — for example:

- perspective
- orthographic projection
- cross-sections
- freehand sketching
- digital camera photos
- isometric projection

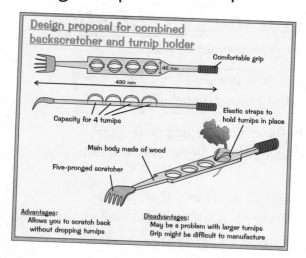

Design proposal for combined backscratcher and turnip holder
Comfortable grip
45 mm
430 mm
Capacity for 4 turnips
Elastic straps to hold turnips in place
Main body made of wood
Five-pronged scratcher
Advantages:
Allows you to scratch back without dropping turnips
Disadvantages:
May be a problem with larger turnips
Grip might be difficult to manufacture

4) Once you've got a few possible designs, you need to check that each one matches your specification — any that don't will not be suitable.

5) Finally, you need to choose one of your suitable designs to develop further.

Write whatever comes to mind — no hope for me then...

Think what someone will need to know to fully appreciate your design, and include this information on your proposal. And remember — you need to do quite a few of these so that you can choose the best one to develop and improve. This is the bit where you need to get your creative head on.

Development

Once you've decided on a design, you can begin to <u>develop</u> it further.
This is when your design should start to really <u>take shape</u>.

You can Develop your Design in Different Ways

Depending on the <u>type</u> of product that's being produced, further development might involve:

Peg protruding from main body...

...and a <u>series of holes</u> in the elastic straps...

...mean that the straps can be <u>adjusted</u> in length by putting the peg through a different hole.

1) producing further <u>sketches</u> — but in more detail e.g. recording the <u>sizes</u> of fittings and components, and dimensions for <u>component positions</u>. Also sketching how parts should be <u>constructed</u> and <u>fitted together</u>.

2) <u>modelling</u> and <u>testing</u> your idea. Or <u>experimenting</u> with different aspects of the design. E.g. you could try various materials, sizes and production methods.

3) using <u>people's opinions</u> about developments to help you arrive at a satisfactory solution.

Modelling means Trying Things Out

It can be useful to <u>prototype</u> or <u>model</u> your idea, especially if it's difficult to draw.

1) Try out <u>different aspects</u> of your design. If your design is quite complex it may help to break it down into smaller, more manageable parts and test them individually.

2) Use a camera (digital or otherwise) to <u>record</u> your models.

3) <u>Evaluate</u> the models (see next page), <u>identifying reasons</u> for selecting or rejecting different designs.

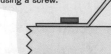

The peg was originally made using a nail, but when the elastic was pulled, the nail came out of the wood too easily.

This was remedied by using a screw.

This is a vital part of the design process. Ideally you should <u>solve all the potential problems</u> with your design at this stage.

Use the Results to Make Modifications

1) Results from your modelling and from your evaluation (see next page) will help you make important <u>modifications</u> (changes) to improve the product, and help it meet the design <u>specification</u>.

2) Suggested improvements could be:
   • ways to make the <u>product itself better</u>,
   • suggestions to make it more suitable for <u>mass production</u> (see page 48).

3) But make sure you keep a <u>record</u> of whatever it is you find out (see next page).

4) Once you've made a modification to your design, you'll need to <u>try it out</u> to see if it actually improves things.

5) You might find that you end up modifying something, then trying it out, then making another modification and trying that out, then making another modification and trying that out, and so on. That's just the way it goes sometimes.

Modification — wear a parka and ride a scooter...

Modelling and evaluation (see next page) go hand in hand. It's pointless building a model and trying it out if you're not going to bother learning anything from it. So keep your thinking trousers on at all times and make the most of your modelling time.

Evaluation

Evaluation's an important part of any product development process, and needs to be done at various stages along the way.

Keep Records of your Research and Testing

1) As you develop your product, keep records of any testing or market research you do. Write it all down, keep it, and refer back to it.

2) You might have tested materials for suitability, or tested components to see how well they work — but whatever you did, you need to write down all the results.

3) Compare the good and bad points of existing products with your model or prototype. Ask yourself if your product does the job better. Record your results.

4) Find out people's opinions and preferences about your models and prototypes (see previous page). This will help you to refine your ideas so you can arrive at the best solution.

5) Questionnaires help here — relevant market research questions might include:

> • Does the product work well?
> • Does the product work as well as similar products on the market?
> • Does the product look good? Is it well styled and modern-looking?
> • Are you unsure about any of the features? If so, which ones and why?
> • If this product were on the market, would you consider buying it?
> • If you were buying it, which price range do you think it would fall into?
> • Do you prefer another similar product to this one?

So would you consider buying one?

This type of evaluation is called formative evaluation — it's being used to help form the final design.

Now You should Know Exactly What You're Making

By the time you've finished developing your ideas and have arrived at a final design, you should have found out / worked out:

1) The best materials, tools and other equipment to use (and their availability). This might include identifying any pre-manufactured components you're going to use.

2) The approximate manufacturing time needed to make each item.

3) How much it should cost to manufacture each item.

4) The most appropriate assembly process — this is going to be important information when it comes to planning production, and can be in the form of a flow chart (see page 8).

If you don't know what you're doing now, you never will...

At this stage of the process it should be crystal clear in your own mind how your final product should look, and how you're going to make it. But you're not finished yet. No, no, no, no, no... There's still the little business of actually making your pride and joy. Oh what fun... what fun...

Manufacturer's Specification

Now that you know <u>exactly</u> what you're going to make, you need to <u>communicate</u> all that info to the person who's actually going to <u>make</u> it.

You need to produce a Manufacturer's Specification

A manufacturer's specification can be a written <u>series of statements</u>, or <u>working drawings</u> and <u>sequence diagrams</u>. It has to explain <u>exactly</u> how the product will be made, and should include:

1) clear <u>construction</u> details explaining <u>exactly</u> how each bit's going to be made,

2) <u>sizes</u> — <u>precise measurements</u> of each part,

3) <u>tolerances</u> — the maximum and minimum sizes each part should be,

4) <u>finishing</u> details — any special sequences for finishing,

5) <u>quality control</u> instructions — where, when and how the manufacturing process should be checked, (See page 8 for time planning and page 41 for quality control.)

6) <u>costings</u> — how much each part costs, and details of any other costs involved.

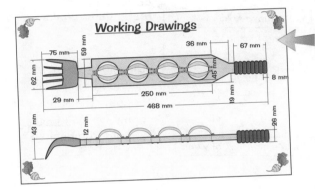

<u>Working drawings</u> give the precise <u>dimensions</u> of the product.

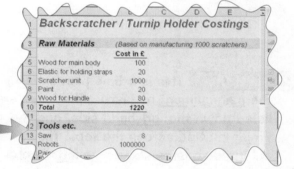

<u>Spreadsheets</u> are great for working out <u>costings</u>.

Plan how long the Production Process should take

When you get to this stage of product development, you also need to plan:

1) how your methods might have to <u>change</u> to produce the product <u>in volume</u>

2) <u>each stage</u> of the process in a great deal of <u>detail</u>

3) <u>how long</u> each stage will take

4) what needs to be <u>prepared</u> before you can start each stage

5) how you will <u>ensure consistency</u> and <u>quality</u>

See the <u>next page</u> as well for some different ways to help with this planning.

Clear construction details — "Insert tab A into slot B..."*

You know what they say... the devil's in the detail. Yeah, well, I don't know exactly what that means, but it's probably got something to do with being really precise. And that's what you've got to do with your manufacturer's specification, or your masterpiece could end up as a dog's dinner.

* ...which doesn't fit, so try it in every other slot before widening slot B until it does actually fit. Repeat for tabs C, D and E.

Planning Production

Making one or two examples of your product is (relatively) easy. But mass-producing it is a whole different ball game. And it takes a shed-load of careful planning.

Use Charts to help you

You need to work out <u>how long</u> each stage will take, and how these times will fit into the <u>total time</u> you've allowed for production. There are different ways of doing this:

① **Work Order** This can be produced as a <u>table</u> or <u>flow chart</u>. The purpose of a work order is to plan <u>in sequence</u> each task to be carried out. This will also include: tools and equipment, quality control stages, safety, and so on.

Day	Process	Tools needed
1	Cut main block of wood	Panel saw
	Cut 4 turnip-holder holes	Drill, fret saw
2	Paint main block of wood	Paint, paint brush

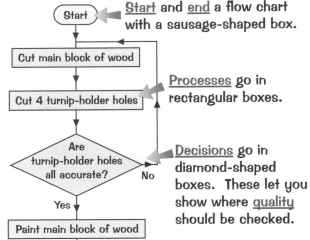

<u>Start</u> and <u>end</u> a flow chart with a sausage-shaped box.

<u>Processes</u> go in rectangular boxes.

<u>Decisions</u> go in diamond-shaped boxes. These let you show where <u>quality</u> should be checked.

② **Gantt Chart** This is a time plan showing the <u>management</u> of tasks. The tasks are listed down the <u>left-hand</u> side, and the <u>timing</u> plotted across the top. The coloured squares show <u>how long</u> each task takes, and the <u>order</u> they're done in.

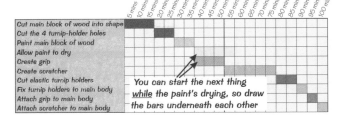

You can start the next thing <u>while</u> the paint's drying, so draw the bars underneath each other

Test that the Product Works and Meets the Specification

1) When you think you've got the final product, it's vital to <u>test</u> it. Most important of all, you have to make sure it <u>works</u>, and meets the original <u>design specification</u>.

2) More <u>questionnaires</u> or <u>surveys</u> may help here. Ask a wide range of people to give their opinions about the finished product.

3) If your product <u>fails</u> to match any part of the <u>specification</u>, you must explain <u>why</u>. You really have to stand back and have a good hard think about your work. If you aren't satisfied with the way any part of the process went, think of how you could put it right for next time. Write it down in the form of a report.

4) This type of final evaluation is called <u>summative evaluation</u> — it summarises what you've learnt.

There's nothing like a good chart...

So, that's all you have to do when it comes to your project. Just do in a few short weeks pretty much what it takes people in industry several months to complete, and you've got no worries.

9

Revision Summary for Section One

So that's the section over with, and what a roller-coaster ride full of fun and excitement it was. Yeah, well, the fun's not over yet, so don't look so disappointed. There's still some exciting revision questions for you to tackle. So try the questions, and then have a look back through the section to see if you got them all right. If you did — great. But if you got any wrong, have another careful read of the section and then <u>try the questions again</u>. And keep doing this until you can get all the questions right. That way, you know you're learning stuff.

1) What is the name given to the whole process of designing and making something?

2) Give three reasons why a new product might be needed.

3) Describe the kind of information you should put in your design brief.

4) Give three ways in which research can help you when you're designing a new product.

5) Explain how a questionnaire can be useful.

6) Give two other methods you could use to carry out research.

7) What is the name given to the process of drawing conclusions from your research?

8) Explain what is meant by a design specification.

9) Why might some points in a design specification be hard to assess just by looking at the product?

10) When would you compile an initial design specification?

11) Give three ways of getting started on your ideas.

12) What does the word 'annotate' mean?

13) What information should you include in your designs?

14) Why should you aim to produce a number of design ideas?

15) Give three techniques for presenting your designs.

16) Name two ways of developing your designs further.

17) Explain why it's useful to model your designs.

18) Describe two kinds of improvement you could make to your design.

19) When should you make an evaluation of your design? a) at the end of the project
b) throughout the project   c) evaluation is for wimps and sissies.

20) Describe two ways of evaluating your work.

21) What is meant by the phrase 'formative evaluation'?

22) Explain why a manufacturer's specification needs to be very precise.

23) Give four kinds of information that need to be on a manufacturer's specification.

24) When using a Gantt chart, what information goes down the left-hand side?

25) Describe two methods of planning how long the manufacturing process should take.

26) Describe the process of 'summative evaluation'.

Section One — The Design Process

Paper and Board

There are loads of different types of <u>paper</u> and <u>board</u> — each designed to suit a particular situation.

Paper — Ones You Need to Know About and Use

1) <u>Cartridge paper</u> has a <u>textured</u> surface, which is great for sketching with pencils, crayons, pastels, gouache, inks and watercolours.

2) <u>Layout paper</u> is <u>thin</u> and <u>translucent</u> (you can see light through it) and is used for general design work — particularly generating ideas.

3) <u>Bleed-proof paper</u> is used by designers when drawing with <u>felt-tips</u> and <u>marker pens</u>. The ink doesn't spread out (<u>bleed</u>) — it stays put.

4) <u>Tracing paper</u> is <u>translucent</u>, and is used to <u>copy images</u>.

5) <u>Photocopy paper</u> is probably the paper you use most in <u>class</u>. It's most commonly used in either <u>A4</u> or <u>A3</u> sizes. It's <u>cheap</u>.

6) <u>Grid paper</u> may have a <u>square</u>, <u>isometric</u> or <u>perspective</u> pre-printed pattern on it — <u>square grid paper</u> is useful for orthographic drawings and <u>nets</u> (for product developments), and <u>isometric grid paper</u> is good for <u>presentation drawings</u>.

square grid paper

isometric grid paper

perspective grid paper

Board — These are the Ones you Need to Know About

The weight of paper and card is measured in <u>gsm</u> (grams per square metre).
Above 200 gsm, it's not paper any more — it's <u>board</u>.

1) <u>Mounting card</u> is used to mount drawings and photographs for presentation or framing — usually by cutting a 'window'.

2) <u>Foamboard</u> (polystyrene foam laminated between card) is lightweight and is used for models and mounting.

3) <u>Solid white board</u> has a high quality bleached surface, which is ideal for printing, and is used loads in primary packaging, i.e. the packaging that's used for individual items (as opposed to secondary packaging, which might be a big box used to transport lots of the same item to shops, etc.).

4) <u>Corrugated card</u> is used a lot in <u>secondary</u> packaging to protect products during transit. It's made up of a <u>fluted inner core</u> sandwiched between <u>two outer layers</u>.

5) <u>Duplex board</u> has a <u>different colour</u> and <u>texture</u> on <u>each side</u>. It's often used where only <u>one surface</u> is <u>seen</u>, so that only one side needs to be <u>smooth</u> for <u>printing</u>. It's <u>unbleached</u>, so it's ideal for <u>food packaging</u>.

6) <u>Klett</u> is a type of <u>corrugated board</u> used in packaging which uses <u>double-sided tape</u> instead of <u>cow gum</u> to bond it together.

Yes, cow gum. As in "made from boiled up cows".

Board is Often Made from Recycled Paper

1) As paper and card are made from wood pulp, most of it's <u>recyclable</u> and from <u>sustainable resources</u>.

2) It's therefore <u>environmentally friendly</u>.

3) A lot of <u>cardboard</u> is made from recycled material.

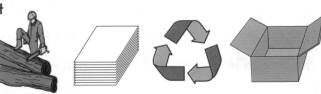

Paper and board — I can't handle the excitement...

Well there it is... a big <u>fat</u> page on paper and board. I don't blame you if you're <u>feeling</u> a bit "bored".
Ha ha, geddit? Anyway, stop moaning — revision isn't about fun. That's why we have <u>Ant and Dec</u>.

Plastics — Types and Uses

Plastics (<u>polymers</u> and <u>copolymers</u>) are <u>synthetic resinous substances</u> that can be <u>moulded</u> with the aid of heat and/or pressure. There are two main classes of plastics:
1) <u>Thermosetting</u> — ones that <u>once moulded cannot be remoulded</u>,
2) <u>Thermoplastics</u> — ones that are <u>moulded</u> by heating and, if heated again, <u>can be remoulded</u>.

Thermoplastics — *Learn These Ones*

1) <u>Acetate</u> (<u>cellulose acetate</u>) is <u>hard</u>, <u>shiny</u> and <u>transparent/translucent</u>. It's used in badge-making, for overhead projector transparencies and packaging.

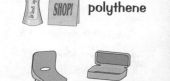
acetate

2) <u>Acrylics</u> (e.g. <u>polymethyl methacrylate</u>, also known as <u>perspex</u> or <u>plexiglas</u>) are <u>hard</u>, <u>shiny</u> and <u>brittle</u>. They're used in schools a lot and come in loads of different colours. They can be used to make menu holders (for example), using a <u>line-bender</u> (see p12), and can also be used to make baths, signs, etc. Acrylics are also used in the paint and textiles industries.

acrylic

3) <u>Polyethylene</u> (or <u>polythene</u>) comes in two main types. <u>Low-density polyethylene</u> (<u>LDPE</u>) is <u>soft</u> and <u>flexible</u> — it's used for packaging, carrier bags, washing-up liquid bottles, etc. <u>High-density polyethylene</u> (<u>HDPE</u>) is <u>stiff</u> and <u>strong</u>, and is used for things like washing-up bowls.

polythene

4) <u>Polyesters</u> (e.g. polyethylene terephthalate — <u>PET</u>) have a variety of uses, e.g. drink bottles and clothes.

polypropylene

5) <u>Polypropylene</u> (<u>PP</u>) is <u>tough</u> and <u>flexible</u>. Products can be made with a '<u>living hinge</u>' (box, lid and hinge all made out of one piece of polypropylene) — which is handy for lunch boxes, etc. It's also used for many different kinds of packaging, chairs, textiles and automotive components.

6) <u>Polystyrene</u> (<u>PS</u>) comes in two main types. <u>Expanded PS</u> (<u>styrofoam</u>) is <u>white</u>, <u>lightweight</u> and <u>crumbly</u>. It is used in <u>protective</u> packaging, <u>insulating</u> packaging and filling for beanbags. It can be shaped easily with a <u>hot-wire cutter</u> to produce accurate 3-D mock-ups and models. <u>Rigid/high impact PS</u> comes in a variety of colours and thicknesses and is used for <u>vacuum forming</u> and <u>fabricating</u> boxes for products.

polystyrene

7) <u>Polyvinyl chloride</u> (<u>PVC</u>) is quite brittle. It's used for <u>blister packs</u>, <u>window frames</u>, <u>vinyl records</u> and <u>interesting clothes</u>.

8) <u>Mylar</u> is a type of <u>polyester film used for stencils</u>.

9) <u>Low-tack masking film</u> is used to position sticky-backed vinyl (cut with computer numerically controlled <u>STIKA</u> or <u>CAMM</u> machines — see p52) onto the chosen surface, e.g. a vehicle. Can also be used for creating <u>signs</u> and <u>stencils</u>.

polyvinyl chloride

10) <u>Corrugated plastic</u>, known as '<u>corriflute</u>', is <u>lightweight</u>, <u>rigid</u> and <u>weatherproof</u>. It's often used for estate agents' sign boards, students' folders, etc.

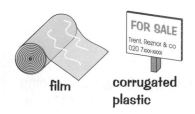
film   corrugated plastic

FOR SALE
Trent, Reznor & co
020 7xxx-xxxx

11) <u>Hard wax</u> has a crumbly texture. It is difficult to mould while dry, but can be melted down and reformed in a mould. It's used in the '<u>lost wax</u>' casting process.

All these chemical names are messing with my brain, man...

This page looks like it was attacked by an over-excited chemist. But I reckon it's <u>bordering on</u> slightly interesting. Anyway, as Ant and Dec would say, "Learn all the plastics on this page and their uses."

Plastics — Manufacturing Techniques

Plastic can be <u>shaped</u> or <u>moulded</u> in loads of different ways:
- You can heat it and bend it (<u>line bending</u>).
- It can be heated and sucked around a mould (<u>vacuum forming</u>).
- It can be heated and blown into a mould (<u>blow moulding</u>), heated and squeezed through a shaped hole (<u>extrusion</u>), or it can be heated and pushed into a hollow mould (<u>injection moulding</u>)...
...to name but a few.

Learn _these_ Five Plastic-Forming Methods

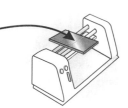

The heating element heats the material along the line where you want to bend it.

1) <u>Line bending</u> (<u>LB</u>) is ideal for use with <u>acrylic sheet</u> — for making picture frames and pencil holders, etc. It can be done <u>manually</u> or with a <u>jig</u> (a tool for cutting/making things accurately) to bend the plastic to a <u>specific angle</u>.

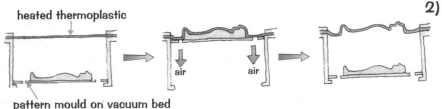

heated thermoplastic

air   air

pattern mould on vacuum bed

2) <u>Vacuum forming</u> (<u>VF</u>) is ideal for use with <u>rigid polystyrene</u> to make trays, casings and containers, e.g. chocolate box trays.

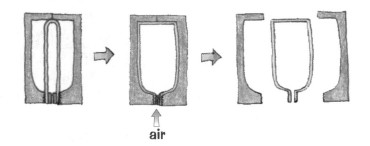

air

3) <u>Blow moulding</u> (<u>BM</u>) uses a <u>two-part mould</u> to make simple hollow objects, like containers for liquids. <u>Blow moulding</u> can also be used with glass, e.g. milk bottles.

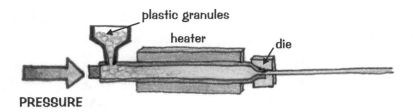

plastic granules

heater   die

PRESSURE

4) <u>Extrusion</u> is ideal for making <u>simple</u>, <u>regular-shaped items</u> like guttering, drain pipes, etc., which can then be cut to a suitable length.

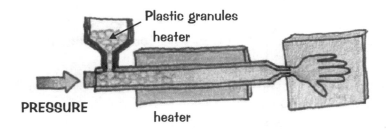

Plastic granules

heater

PRESSURE

heater

5) <u>Injection moulding</u> (<u>IM</u>) is ideal for making <u>complex and highly detailed components</u>, including model kits, seats, and 35 mm film canisters.

Line bending — lots of cowboy types doing yoga...

I'm gonna go out on a limb here — OK, here we go... this stuff is... quite interesting. There — I've said it and I don't feel bad. So <u>learn and sketch</u> it all and learn the uses and all that business.

Smart Materials

Materials that <u>respond to a stimulus</u> (e.g. a change in <u>heat</u>, <u>light</u>, <u>moisture</u> or <u>voltage</u>) can be described as '<u>adaptive</u>', '<u>active</u>', '<u>intelligent</u>' or '<u>smart</u>'.

Materials that <u>do not</u> respond to a stimulus (like <u>wood</u> and <u>stone</u>) can be described as '<u>passive</u>' or '<u>dumb</u>'.

Durr durr durr, I wear my shoes on my nose...

Smart Plastics do All Sorts of Cool Stuff

1) <u>Electro-luminescent panels</u> combine fluorocarbons and phosphorous to <u>produce light</u> (but <u>not heat</u>) when stimulated by <u>electricity</u>.
   Applications include light strips for decorating buildings.

2) <u>Lenticular plastic</u> is an <u>optically embossed film or sheet</u>. Viewed on its lenticular side, it can give the impression that the sheet is <u>thicker than it really is</u>. It's used to make optical effects, and pictures that appear to move when looked at from different angles. It looks a bit like a <u>hologram</u>.

3) <u>Liquid crystal dsplays</u> (<u>LCDs</u>) are made of a material which responds to <u>electrical signals</u>. LCDs are used to make calculator displays and laptop computer screens.

4) <u>Polycaprolactone</u> (sometimes called a <u>polymorph</u>) is a type of plastic used in <u>rapid prototyping</u> (making models to try out new designs). Its <u>low melting point</u> of 62 °C means that it can be made <u>mouldable</u> by immersing it in <u>hot water</u>. Polycaprolactone can be moulded and <u>shaped by hand</u> when warm, or <u>machined</u> when cold. When fully cooled, it looks similar to nylon and is stiffer and stronger than HDPE (see page 11).

If you use polycaprolactone, don't overheat it, or you'll ruin it.

Smart Wire 'Remembers' its Shape

<u>Nitinol</u> is <u>an alloy of nickel and titanium</u>. It is one of a number of alloys that exhibit <u>shape-memory</u> characteristics — i.e. it can be made to <u>remember</u> a particular <u>shape or length</u> and <u>return</u> to it when a particular <u>temperature</u> or <u>voltage</u> is applied. The uses of nitinol smart wire include braces for teeth, spectacle frames, valves, locks and robotic devices.

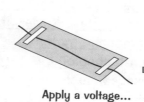
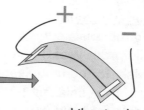

Smart wire shouldn't be overheated, or it'll stop working.

Apply a voltage...

...and the wire shrinks to its original size.

Nitinol actually has a higher IQ than Richard Whiteley...

Mind you, so has Carol Vorderman. Anyway, there are loads of 'smart' plastics and 'smart' wire products out there. And <u>you</u> need to learn <u>what they are</u> and <u>how they work</u>. Oh, yes you do...

Smart Materials

Smart Dyes Change in Response to Heat / Light / Water

1) <u>Photochromic dyes</u> change colour reversibly in response to <u>light</u>.
   Uses include nail polish, yo-yos, T-shirts, etc.

2) <u>Solvation-chromic dyes</u> change colour in response to <u>moisture</u>.
   Products under development include handkerchiefs, nappies and
   hygiene products.

3) <u>Thermochromic dyes</u> change colour reversibly in response to
   <u>changes in temperature</u>. Products include mugs, bubble bath,
   baby spoons, dishes and wine bottle labels.

4) <u>Thermochromic liquid crystal</u> changes colour reversibly in response
   to <u>heat</u>. By a process of <u>micro-encapsulation</u>, the liquid crystal is
   made into an <u>ink</u>, which can be printed onto a <u>substrate</u> (e.g. plastic
   or paper). Uses include battery test panels, warning patches on
   computer chips, and thermometers for fish tanks.

Smart Stuff — it's Stuff that's Smart

Happy Birthday to you...

Happy Birthday

1) <u>IQ Controllers</u> are low-cost self-contained units containing a chip
   capable of switching up to three outputs on and off in a
   pre-programmed sequence. They're used in school D&T work.

2) <u>PICs</u> (<u>Peripheral Interface Controllers</u>) program your <u>own</u>
   <u>integrated circuit</u> (<u>microchip</u>) using a PC to create circuits that
   control project work. PICs are used in industry and are
   embedded in new-style phone cards and credit cards.

3) <u>Piezoelectric materials</u>, e.g. lead zirconate titanate (PZT) or lead
   lanthanite zirconate titanate (PLZT), produce <u>electrical energy</u>
   when a mechanical <u>force</u> is applied — and <u>vice versa</u>. They have a
   variety of applications, including speaker circuits (like you get in
   some greetings cards), inkjet printers, ignition switches and
   intruder alarms (the kind that send a signal to a control centre).

New Modern Materials are Constantly Being Developed

Modern materials <u>enhance</u> the <u>performance</u> of a product. They replace (or are combined with)
natural ingredients in food, and natural fibres in textiles. New <u>materials</u> are continually being
developed through the invention of new or improved processes. These include:

1) biological materials, such as <u>modified enzymes</u>, <u>antioxidants</u>,
   <u>synthetic flavours</u> and <u>genetically engineered foods</u>,

2) strong materials such as <u>carbon fibre</u>, <u>Kevlar fibre</u> (Kevlar is used
   in bulletproof vests) and <u>composite materials</u>,

3) materials for communication technology, e.g. <u>optical fibres</u>,

4) materials for finishing processes, such as <u>Teflon</u>,

5) materials for insulation and clothing, such as <u>neoprene</u>,
   <u>synthetic micro-fibres</u>, <u>Lycra</u> and <u>Polartec</u>.

*The miracle of
Teflon trousers...*

Smart and modern — just like Ikea, really...

I've got a frisbee that changes colour in response to light. It's ace (see page 71 for more about frisbees).
But there's more to smart materials than coloured frisbees. <u>Learn this page</u> — that's what it's for.

Fillers and Finishing

Finishes are things like <u>paint</u>, which are applied to a model or product to <u>protect</u> it from <u>damage</u> and <u>dirt</u> — and to improve its <u>appearance</u>.

But before being painted or varnished, most surfaces need some kind of <u>filling or sanding</u>...

Fillers Prepare Surfaces for Finishing

1) <u>Car-body filler</u> (David's Isopon) is a <u>two-part resin-based product</u>, which, when mixed, sets to a tough finish that can then be machined (i.e. drilled, filed, etc.).

2) <u>Polyfilla</u> is powder that's mixed with water to make a thick paste. This can <u>fill small cracks</u> and <u>improve the surface finish</u> on rough wood and foam models. It sets quickly and can be smoothed with glass paper.

3) <u>Plaster of Paris</u> is a fine white powder, which, when mixed with water, soon sets to a very hard finish. It's used with bandages to set broken limbs and to produce <u>landscape features</u> on <u>scale models</u>. It can be <u>cast in a mould</u>.

4) <u>Art Roc</u> or <u>Modroc</u> is a <u>bandage</u> material <u>impregnated with plaster of Paris</u>. It's great for creating textured landscape surfaces too, particularly when painted.

Laminating and Varnishing Make Work Look Smart

1) <u>Laminating</u> (or <u>encapsulation</u>) is a quick and effective way to finish a piece of work on paper or thin card. Laminating uses heat to <u>sandwich</u> the paper or card between <u>two layers of plastic</u> (see p33). This gives a professional finish to posters, menus, bookmarks, etc.

2) <u>Spirit varnish/lacquers</u> consist of a <u>synthetic</u> (<u>man-made</u>) <u>resin</u> (e.g. acrylic resin, cellulose resin) dissolved in an <u>organic solvent</u>. The solvent evaporates to leave a thin protective layer of varnish. Varnish/lacquer can be applied with a <u>brush</u> or <u>spray can</u>.

Paints are made from Pigment dissolved in a 'Vehicle'

1) <u>Paints</u> are made up of a <u>pigment</u> (a colour) and a 'vehicle' (a solvent — something that <u>carries</u> the pigment).

2) There's a whole load of different 'vehicles', like <u>water</u>, <u>acrylic</u>, <u>cellulose</u>, <u>oil</u>, etc.

3) Once the paint has been applied, the vehicle <u>evaporates</u> to leave just the pigment.

4) Pigments may be made from chemicals, rocks or plants. <u>Woad</u>, which used to be used to dye <u>jeans</u> blue, comes from a <u>plant</u>.

5) Paints can be <u>brushed on</u>, or <u>sprayed on</u> from a can.

Several thin coats of paint, stain, varnish, etc. look better than one thick coat.

I wanted to finish with my girlfriend, so I laminated her... *(Oh come on, you didn't believe me did you...)*

Learn which <u>fillers</u> and <u>finishes</u> are best for <u>which surfaces</u>. You wouldn't want to spoil a model you'd spent ages on by messing up the finish, would you? Oh no, no, no, no.

Drawing and Painting Media

When designing and producing <u>presentation drawings</u> there are <u>loads of different media</u> you can choose from. Mixing your media can produce <u>stunning</u> results — so <u>be daring and experiment</u>.

Pencils are Ace

"You can lead a horse to water but a pencil must be lead." (Stan Laurel)

<u>Pencils</u> are classified by their <u>hardness</u> (<u>H</u>) and <u>blackness</u> (<u>B</u>) and range from <u>9H</u> to <u>9B</u>. An <u>HB</u> pencil is in the middle as it's both hard and black, and is good for general sketching. A harder pencil (like a <u>2H</u>) is better for <u>precise, technical drawings</u> as it won't smudge so easily.

1) Pencils are made from a mixture of <u>graphite</u> (a form of carbon) and clay.
2) <u>Coloured pencils</u> come in a range of colours and a variety of hardnesses. The <u>softer</u> ones are best for laying <u>even, flat colour</u> and are less likely to <u>break</u>.

The more graphite, the blacker (and softer) the pencil.

Inks, Paints, Pastels, Dry-Transfer Lettering... also Ace

ink

"Blood Of Your Enemies" Ink.

pastels

1) Inks are pigments suspended in water or solvent. They're good for <u>colour infilling</u>, <u>background washes</u> and <u>writing</u> (obviously).
2) <u>Gouache</u> is a type of <u>opaque paint</u>, which is ideal for producing <u>flat areas of colour</u>, or <u>highlights</u> on renderings (e.g. coats of plaster, mortar, etc.).
3) <u>Pastels</u> come in two varieties — <u>oil and chalk</u>. <u>Chalk pastel</u> is particularly good for producing <u>backgrounds</u> on <u>renderings</u>, or adding <u>tone and shading</u>. It's easily blended using your fingers or cotton wool.
4) <u>Dry-transfer lettering</u> is applied with pressure from a waxed translucent sheet onto drawings or prototype models. It comes in various <u>typefaces</u>, <u>sizes</u>, <u>styles</u> and <u>colours</u>.

Airbrushes Blow a Mist of Ink

1) <u>Airbrushes</u> blow a <u>fine mist of ink</u> from a reservoir onto an image area, using <u>compressed air</u> from a compressor or a 'power pack' (can of compressed air).
2) It's a <u>time-consuming</u> medium — you have to mask all the areas you don't want to airbrush using a low-tack clear film and a craft knife. Plus you need <u>loads of practice</u> to do it well.
3) You can get really great <u>photo-realistic</u> results, if you know what you're doing. There are excellent examples of airbrushing on various record/CD sleeves, posters and adverts.
4) Airbrushing <u>effects</u> can also be achieved with some <u>computer packages</u>, e.g. <u>Adobe Photoshop</u>.

Felt Pens and Markers — Water-Based or Spirit-Based

<u>Water-based</u> pens aren't suitable for <u>large areas</u> because they dry quickly and leave <u>streaks</u>.

1) <u>Fine-liners</u> come in a variety of thicknesses and colours. They're <u>great</u> for <u>outlining drawings</u>.
2) <u>Markers</u> are available in hundreds of different colour tones. They can have <u>chisel</u>, <u>bullet</u> and <u>brush tips</u> to offer greater flexibility of application. Popular brands include Magic Markers and <u>Pantone</u>. Pantone guarantee <u>colour-matching</u> across <u>all their media</u> — card, paper, paint, printing ink, etc. — meaning their 'dark green' paint is exactly the same colour as their 'dark green' card.
3) <u>Technical pens</u> are used for drawing <u>fine</u>, <u>precise lines</u>, e.g. orthographic drawings. They can be <u>expensive</u> and <u>difficult to master</u>.

Ooh, colouring in — fantastic...

For the <u>best results</u>, use the <u>best quality</u> pencils and marker pens you can lay your hands on — you get what you pay for. Though I guess that kind of goes without saying. Happy colouring in...

Drawing and Painting Equipment

Drawing things is much easier if you use the right equipment.

Drawing Boards — for Easier, Better Drawing

1) Drawing boards can be as simple as a sheet of blockboard or plywood.
2) The more sophisticated and expensive ones are free-standing and include a mechanism to adjust the angle of the board.
3) Some also include an integrated parallel motion or T-square.

Set Squares, Rulers and Protractors — for Marking Angles

1) Set squares, as the name suggests, have angles which are set. The 30-60-90° set square is pretty much essential for isometric and planometric projection. The 45-45-90° set square is essential for oblique and axonometric projections. Both are useful for orthographic projection (see page 37).

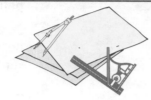

Yeah, hun, yeah.
Bring your
set square.
Love you too.

2) Rulers (or rules) are usually either 150 or 300 mm in length and made from steel, polypropylene or wood. They're used mainly for measuring and providing a straight edge. A steel safety rule is shaped so as to protect the user's fingers when cutting or scoring card and paper.

3) Protractors are used to measure angles in degrees. They're useful for drawing pie charts.

Clean your set squares and T-squares regularly, or you'll end up with smudges everywhere.

Compasses Draw Circles and Bisect Lines

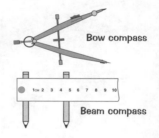

Bow compass

Beam compass

1) Compasses let you draw accurate arcs and circles of varying diameters.
2) They can also be used to bisect a line (divide it in half).
3) Bow compasses are more accurate than those with an attached pencil. Beam compasses allow large arcs and circles to be drawn.

Curves and Templates — for Drawing Curvy Shapes

Curves and templates are used to speed up the drawing of complex and repetitive shapes.

1) French curves (or ship's curves) are curved templates used by designers to draw a variety of complex curves (and profiles for ships, hence the name).

French curve

flexicurve

2) Flexicurves are a variation on a French/ship's curve and can be shaped and reshaped to provide limitless profiles. Very exciting.

3) Ellipse and circle templates are used to quickly produce ellipses and circles of varying sizes. Good good good.

circle template

4) Eraser guides are used to protect a drawing while using an eraser to remove pencil marks. Eraser guides make it easy to leave a highlight or tidy edge when erasing.

Why do I need templates? — surely one's enough...

It's a good job you're not expected to draw perfect straight lines and perfect circles on your own. What a nightmare that'd be. So just remember to use all these bits of kit when you need them.

Adhesives

There are loads of different adhesives and glues to choose from. Each one's suited to a particular use or situation. I bet you never knew how exciting adhesives could be.

Learn About and Use these Adhesives

1) Glue sticks are commonly used in schools to bond paper and card as they're non-toxic, cheap and come in a range of handy sizes. Common brands include Pritt, UHU and Bostik. They're all clear when dry and are environmentally friendly.

2) Unlike glue sticks (which are solid) the glue sold in squeezy tubes (glue pens) is liquid and can be messy to use. Glue pens also bond paper and card and are clear when dry.

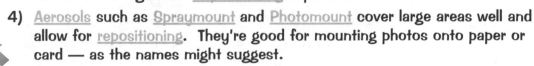

3) Rubber-based cement (or gum) is a latex-based glue. The glue should be applied to both surfaces and left for about ten minutes before bringing the surfaces together. Repositioning is possible.

4) Aerosols such as Spraymount and Photomount cover large areas well and allow for repositioning. They're good for mounting photos onto paper or card — as the names might suggest.

5) Superglue comes in small tubes and quickly bonds a large variety of materials, e.g. ceramics, plastics, textiles and metal. But you have to take care not to glue your fingers together.

6) Polyvinyl-acetate (PVA) glue is a water-based glue used for bonding wood. It's also good for gluing paper and card, though it takes a while to dry.

7) Epoxy resin glue (e.g. Araldite) is a two-part adhesive — with a resin and a hardener. 'Rapid' versions set in about 5 minutes, so speed is essential.

8) Balsa cement, as the name implies, is good for sticking balsa wood. It's clear when dry.

9) Acrylic cement (Tensol Number 12), as its name suggests, is used to bond acrylic.

10) Glue guns are mains powered and use a low-melt plastic to quickly bond materials like wood, fabric and card together. The glue will burn you if it gets on your skin, so take care.

There's Sticky Tape and Blu-Tack, Too

1) Sticky-backed plastic can be used to cover and protect large awkwardly shaped card and paper models when lamination isn't possible. Blue Peter eat your heart out.

2) Masking tape, Sellotape and double-sided tape all come on rolls. Masking tape is removable low-tack tape, used to stick paper to drawing boards or to mask areas when using pastels or markers. Sellotape is used for general sticking of card and paper. Double-sided tape is best used to stick card models and shape nets. It's good if you want the join hidden from view.

3) Blu-tack and white-tack are for temporary fixing — used mainly for sticking posters to walls, but also for folder work to allow for the repositioning of layouts.

Stickier than a sticky thing in a basket of sticks...

Once again, there are simply bucket-loads of ways of doing something, and you have to figure out which one suits your needs best. Take your time. There's no rush. Spraymount? Bingo.

Section Two — Materials and Components

Cutting Tools

There are many <u>cutting tools</u> available to manipulate <u>card</u> and <u>paper</u>, and make <u>models</u>. The following tools are ones you currently use, will use, or will need to know about.

Good Old *Scissors* Cut *Paper* and *Thin Card*

<u>Scissors</u> are probably the first cutting tool you ever used. They cut <u>paper</u> and <u>thin card</u> well, but are not suited to cutting <u>very fine detail</u> and <u>removing</u> bits from within a sheet of paper or card. Safety scissors have rounded ends and 'pinking shears' produce an interesting zigzag edge *(which also helps stop material from fraying, so pinking shears are often used for things like fabric swatches).*

Craft Knives Cut *Card* and *Paper*

There are loads of different <u>craft</u>/<u>trimming</u>/<u>hobby knives</u> on the market, and different schools use different types. Styles include <u>surgical scalpels</u>, <u>Stanley knives</u>, and other 'generic' types. Some have <u>retractable blades</u> or <u>blade covers</u> for <u>safety</u> when not in use. All are mainly used to cut card and paper, though some will cut thick board, balsa wood, etc.

Compass Cutters Cut *Arcs* and *Circles*

<u>Compass cutters</u> are used to cut arcs and circles in card and paper. Unlike a 'circle cutter' you can vary the diameter of the arc or circle to be cut. <u>Use with a cutting mat</u>.

Rotary Cutters and Guillotines Cut *Large Sheets*

<u>Rotary cutters</u> (also known as rotatrims or paper trimmers) cut large sheets of paper and card, often <u>many sheets at a time</u>. They cut in a straight line to produce a nice straight edge. <u>Guillotines</u> do the same thing, but they have a large blade that you push down.

Modelling Materials need *Special Cutters*

You may wish to use styrofoam, thin plywood or MDF in your models. <u>Styrofoam</u> is best cut with a <u>hot-wire cutter</u>. <u>Plywood</u> and <u>MDF</u> are easily cut using a <u>fret saw</u> or <u>coping saw</u>. A <u>Hegner saw</u> (a kind of jigsaw with a very thin blade) is a quicker option and gives excellent results with care.

Safety Equipment *is Really Important*

When using a <u>craft knife</u> or any sharp-bladed cutting tool, it's best to use a <u>cutting mat</u> (to protect your work surface) and a <u>safety rule</u> (to protect your fingers). When cutting <u>styrofoam</u> and <u>MDF</u>, make sure there's plenty of <u>ventilation</u> and extraction — and wear a mask.

When using cutting equipment, always take appropriate safety precautions.

Die Cutters and Creasing Bars *Cut Shapes*

<u>Die cutters</u> are commercial cutters (not unlike pastry cutters) which <u>cut out</u> materials for packaging. <u>Creasing bars</u> add <u>creases</u> *(no, really?)*, which makes the material easier to fold.

Just remember — the guillotine is for paper, not heads...

<u>Take care</u> when cutting. Not only will the result be better — but you won't get <u>blood</u> on it...

Tools and Materials

It's dead important to use the right tool for a job.
It makes it easier for you, and will mean the final result is better.

Cut Wood with a Saw — but choose the right kind

1) Coping saw — this small saw can be used to cut wood and plastic in curved and irregular shapes.

2) Piercing saw — This is very similar to a coping saw, but is quite weak due to its thin blade. It can also be used on metals and plastics.

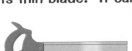 3) Tenon saw — good for sawing materials to length, e.g. dowelling.

4) Bench-mounted vibro saw — this is an electric version of a piercing/coping saw. It's also used on plastics.

5) Glasspaper — this is used to put a very smooth surface finish on a variety of materials.

6) Surform tools — there are a load of different handtools all under the heading "Surform" tools (it's a brand name). They include files and planes and they're used for shaping wood and plaster.

You might need Special Tools to Work with Plastic

This bloke from that famous 1980s band (I can't remember their name) demonstrates how to use a big fancy saw.

1) Vacuum former — this machine moulds polystyrene to a desired shape using pre-made patterns/formers (see also page 12).

2) Scraper — this creates a smooth finish on the edges of acrylic, but it can also be used on wood.

3) Wet and dry paper — this is used after filing (first when the paper is dry, and then when it's wet) to achieve a very smooth finish. It can be used on acrylic and metals too.

4) Hot wire cutter — this can be used on expanded polystyrene foam and rigid foam to shape with a smooth surface finish.

Metalwork also needs some Special Tools

1) Files — these are used to create a smooth finish on metals and plastics. A variety of shapes and tooth sizes are available.

2) Needle files — these are also used to create smooth finishes, but they're much finer and so are better for detailed work.

3) Twist-drill bits — these are for creating holes in metal, wood and plastic. They come in various sizes, and are used in pillar, bench-mounted or hand drills.

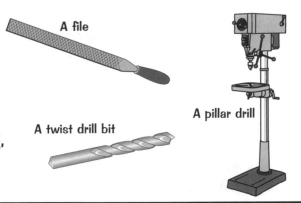

A file

A twist drill bit

A pillar drill

This page is at the cutting edge of D&T revision material...

Never forget to use the right tools when you're working with materials. And when you're cutting stuff, it's a good idea to sing a good cutting song — like this one, for example: "I like cut cut cutting" (sung to the tune of Ay Ay Ay Ay Moosy, the legendary 1980s new romantic club anthem).

Fixings

Fixings are for joining materials together. Some methods of fixing can join a number of different types of materials. There are also specific fixings designed to suit a particular material — e.g. corrijoints, which are bits of injection-moulded plastic used to join plastic corrugated board.

Learn About all these kinds of Fixings

1) Ratchet rivets and rapid-assembly post and screw fixings are designed to join sheets of corriflute (corrugated plastic) together. Both fixings push together to form a secure joint.

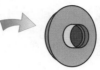

2) Eyelets are used to join pieces of card together whilst providing a movable joint. This is great for making card mechanisms, e.g. linkages *(see also p58)*. The eyelets are applied using a special punch.

3) Prong paper fasteners are used to join pieces of paper and card together. The fastener is inserted through a hole and then opened out. Like eyelets, they can make movable joints for card mechanisms and linkages.

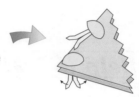

> Sometimes paperclips can be very useful... but not all the time.

4) Paperclips are a temporary fixing for a number of pieces of paper or thin card.

5) Staples are a permanent or temporary fixing for a number of pieces of paper or thin card. Staples can be removed with a staple-remover.

6) Velcro pads are self-adhesive pieces of the famous two-part hook and loop system. They have hundreds of different uses and are particularly good for display purposes. Hooray for Velcro, eh.

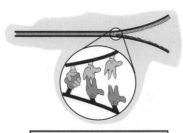

> Using a microscope, the simplicity of velcro is easy to see.

7) Drawing pins (also known as thumb tacks or mapping pins) are useful for sticking paper and card to display boards.

8) Press stud fastenings are good for joining fabric bits together.

Ma, I'm fixin' to learn this here page...

You're supposed to be able to say which fixing would be best to use for any given situation. What that means for you right now is that you have to learn all the fixings on this page. Ha ha haa.

Ways of Producing Work

If you go to an office Christmas party, the photocopier will probably be used to... err...
...make copies of the invitations. Yes, that's it.

Photocopiers are Used to Reproduce Work

Photocopying is a 'dry' printing process. This means that no liquids are present — the ink (toner)
is a powder, that 'bonds' to the paper when it's heated inside the machine.

Photocopiers have many functions. Many can:

1) enlarge and reduce an original image, up to A3 size,

2) print onto thin, textured paper, card or acetate,

3) automatically collate a number of documents
— i.e. put the pages in the right order,

4) print double-sided,

5) print from double-sided documents,

6) punch holes and staple.

*Use photocopiers to quickly and cheaply reproduce
'borders' for your project work or copy images from
books and catalogues for use in development work.*

Light Boxes Help to Trace Images Accurately

Light boxes are exactly what you'd expect — boxes with a light in them...

1) Just put the image you want to trace on top of the light
box, a piece of paper over that, and hey presto — you
can see the original image really easily.

2) Tracing images is useful to copy parts of a design or plan
quickly and accurately.

Desktop Publishing is Page Layout by Computer

1) Desktop publishing is when you do newspaper, book and magazine layout on computer rather
than by hand. DTP packages, like QuarkXPress, Adobe PageMaker and Microsoft Publisher,
allow for increased speed and creativity. Ideas can be tried out and then changed in
seconds.

2) DTP packages allow for multiple layers of colour and images to be
created. They make it easy to add text which flows or
'wraps around' a photograph or image.

3) Images are usually imported into DTP packages from other programs,
like Adobe Photoshop, Adobe Illustrator or CorelDraw.

This book was laid out in Adobe PageMaker, by the way.

Functions of a photocopier — wow, what a fascinating page...

Photocopiers and light boxes are there to help you produce work quickly and easily,
so take the hint and use them when necessary. And get used to using DTP — it rocks.

Revision Summary for Section Two

"So, Mr Bond, we meet again." That's what that bad guy said when he came face to face with his arch-enemy for a second time. Just like a set of revision questions meeting you for a second time. OK, so revision questions may not be quite the same thing as a world-domination-seeking baddie, but you know what I mean. So do the James Bond thing — get the girl and kill the revision questions. Or something...

Hmm... Getting a bit lost in that metaphor.
(Sigh) Just ignore me and get on with the questions, OK.

1) In what units are the weights of paper and card measured?

2) Describe duplex board, and say why it's used extensively in food packaging.

3) Describe the main difference between a thermoplastic and a thermosetting plastic.

4) What are the two main types of polyethylene? Describe their properties.

5) Why is expanded polystyrene used as a packaging material?

6) What is corriflute? Describe a couple of uses of this material.

7) Describe five plastic-forming methods.

8) With which plastic-forming method would you produce complex, highly detailed components?

9) Describe the properties of: a) electro-luminescent panels, b) polymorph.

10) Explain the cool properties of Nitinol, a smart wire. What is it used for?

11) Name three stimuli that smart dyes can respond to.

12) What are piezoelectric materials? In what products might you find them?

13) Name four fillers, and describe when they might be used.

14) Give two reasons why a finish might be applied to a product.

15) What is a 'vehicle', in terms of paint?

16) What two letters are used to classify pencils? What's the significance of each letter?

17) Why are water-based felt pens not suitable for covering large areas?

18) Explain when it might be a good idea to use a safety ruler.

19) Describe the properties and uses of:
    a) glue sticks, b) rubber-based cement, c) superglue, d) PVA glue, e) epoxy resin glue.

20) Describe when you might use: a) a craft knife, b) a rotary cutter, c) a die cutter.

21) Name four types of saw, and describe their uses.

22) Explain when you might use a hot-wire cutter.

23) Name two types of fixing that allow you to make linkages in card.

24) Explain how Velcro works.

25) Describe five things a modern top-of-the-range photocopier can do.

26) Desbribe how DTP packages have speeded up the process of producing publications.

What Designers Do...

Graphic design is all about <u>communicating ideas</u> through <u>pictures</u>.
This section's all about different ways of doing just that. And it's one <u>rollercoaster ride</u> of fun, too.

You can Communicate Ideas by Drawing

1) Designers <u>communicate</u> their ideas through drawings.

2) The drawings include <u>notes</u> and <u>annotations</u> to explain details.

3) They're used in <u>meetings</u> with clients to explain concepts.

Prototypes are Models of the Product

1) Prototypes are sometimes refered to as <u>mock-ups</u>.

2) They're produced to <u>explain a concept</u> in 3-D.

3) Producing a prototype makes sure the designs are fully <u>understood</u>.

4) They're usually produced <u>to scale</u>.

Find a Gap in the Market to Promote a New Product

1) Before launching a new product, you need to find a <u>gap in the market</u>.

2) This is an area where, at present, there's no product available to meet the <u>customers' needs</u>.

3) The new product then needs to be <u>promoted</u> in a way that looks <u>attractive</u> to the <u>target customer</u>.

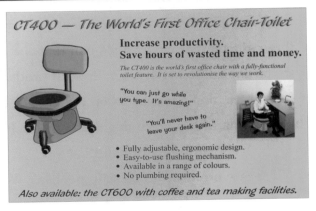

CT400 — The World's First Office Chair-Toilet

Increase productivity.
Save hours of wasted time and money.

The CT400 is the world's first office chair with a fully-functional toilet feature. It is set to revolutionise the way we work.

"You can just go while you type. It's amazing!"

"You'll never have to leave your desk again."

- Fully adjustable, ergonomic design.
- Easy-to-use flushing mechanism.
- Available in a range of colours.
- No plumbing required.

Also available: the CT600 with coffee and tea making facilities.

Advertising needs to Attract the Customer

1) There are many <u>different techniques</u> used to <u>promote</u> a new product.

2) They include following <u>trends</u> in <u>fashion</u>. This encourages the customer to buy the product in order to appear <u>trendy</u> and up to date.

3) When a friend has bought a product, <u>peer pressure</u> may influence you to buy the product too.

Dan wasn't convinced by the latest fashion trend.

With the CT400, I shall make billions...

You can't just start building as soon as you've had an idea. You need to <u>design it</u> on paper first, thinking about <u>all the details</u>. Then make a <u>prototype</u> to see exactly how it'll look and work. Imagine if I started mass production of my CT400 and then realised I'd forgotten the <u>flush handle</u>...

Sketching

You don't always have to use perfect drawings. Freehand sketches are fine for getting across initial ideas. And they're much easier to do, so you can get new thoughts on paper quickly.

Freehand Sketching is Very Quick

1) Freehand drawing is where you don't use any drawing equipment apart from a pencil or pen.

2) It's the quickest method of illustration and is handy for getting initial ideas down on paper.

3) 3-D freehand sketches often show how the whole object would look, while 2-D drawings tend to show the details of an object.

Always Start 2-D Sketches with Rectangles and Squares

Standard sketching is very similar to freehand sketching, except that you start by ruling guidelines.

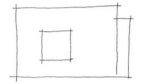
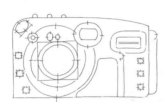

1) Using vertical and horizontal lines you can create squares and rectangles.
2) Use these to draw the outline of your shape first.
3) Details can be added by drawing more squares and rectangles.
4) Add circles and ellipses where necessary.

1) Circles are drawn in square boxes and ellipses are drawn in rectangular boxes.
2) Mark half way along each side.
3) Join the points to form the circle or ellipse.

3-D Sketches are Done Using Crating

Crating is drawing where you start by drawing a box, or 'crate', then gradually adding bits on and taking bits off till you get the exact shape.

1) When you're sketching a 3-D object, it's easier if you imagine it as a basic shape.

2) First you draw the basic geometric shape faintly.

3) Try to stick to a particular drawing technique like 2-pt perspective or isometric.

4) The object can then be drawn within the box.

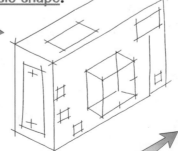
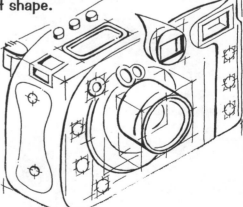

5) Details of the object can be added by drawing more geometric shapes on top.

I love sketching — it's crate...

So remember — always start by drawing the outline of the object. Keep checking the proportions and don't start adding the details until you're sure all the bits are the right size and shape.

Sketching

A designer would use a combination of 2-D and 3-D sketches. Learn 'em all...

Any 3-D Shape can Start Out as a Cuboid

You can remove sections from a cube to make any other 3-D shape.

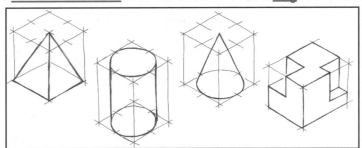

1) Circles and ellipses are completed the same way as in 2-D.

2) Draw a square using the chosen drawing technique.

3) Mark halfway along each edge.

4) Join the points.

To Draw More Accurately use a Grid

1) Grids can be laid under your page to improve the accuracy of your drawing.
   (Or you could just draw on graph/grid paper.)

2) You could use an isometric grid, perspective grid or a square grid.

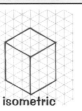

isometric

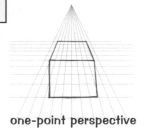

one-point perspective

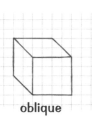

oblique

Wireframe Drawings Aren't Shaded

1) When you draw using the crating technique (see p25), you can leave the solid sides of the shape unshaded.

2) Doing this lets you see straight through the object.

3) You can also view an object in wireframe in CAD software, like the camera shown here:

4) This could be used to show details on all faces of an object.

Develop Ideas with Sketches

1) Freehand sketching's very quick (as you know from p25).

2) You can combine 2-D and 3-D sketches to explain details.

3) And you can add notes to explain details further.

Eeee look at that pyramid — when I last saw 'im 'e were just a cube...

What a funky, groovy and, well, downright sexy page. That's what I think, anyway. Learn the types of sketch here and practise using them — then you can use them in your project. Fantastico.

Enhancement — Shading

You can use various techniques to <u>enhance</u> a drawing.
You can change the <u>thickness of lines</u> or add <u>shading</u> to make parts of the drawing <u>stand out</u>.

Pencil Shading can be Used to Accentuate Shape

1) <u>Shading</u> can be added to a shape to make it look <u>3-D</u>.

2) Different <u>pencils</u> can be used to create different <u>tones</u>.

3) A <u>soft pencil</u> will create a <u>wider tonal variation</u>.

4) Shading a drawing to show <u>depth</u>, <u>light and shade</u> or <u>texture</u> is called <u>rendering</u>.

5) Think about where the light's coming from — make areas furthest from the light the darkest.

You can Use a Pencil to Shade in Different Ways

1) You can <u>shade shapes</u> using a normal <u>pencil</u> in a number of different ways.

2) Using different types of shading is useful for differentiating <u>parts</u> of an object.

1) When you shade using <u>dots</u>, you need to use a <u>different concentration of dots</u> on each side. Dot-matrix printers use this method, but it's fairly <u>time-consuming</u> by hand.

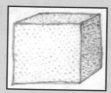

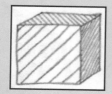

2) In order to shade using <u>lines</u>, you need to use <u>lines at different spacing</u> on each side. Lines at <u>different angles</u> can be used to show different colours, materials, etc.

3) Here's a <u>quick and easy</u> method to give the impression of <u>solidity</u>: If you can see <u>both surfaces</u> that form a line, draw it <u>thin</u>. If you can only see <u>one surface</u>, draw a <u>thick line</u>.

4) <u>Highlights</u> are used to suggest a highly <u>reflective</u> surface. They can be added by leaving <u>white</u> areas.

Could the real Slim Shady please add some highlights to this cube...

This shading stuff's great fun. But you should expect that — this *is* Graphic Products, not <u>maths</u>.
Don't get lost in the wave of pleasure this page brings you — you still need to <u>learn</u> and <u>practise</u> it all.

Enhancement — Surfaces and Textures

When shading shapes you can also use different techniques to represent
different materials — e.g. adding textures, varying the tone and colour, etc.

You can Use Colour and Shading to Represent Surfaces

Wood — use Colour and Draw a Grain...

1) Wood can be done using coloured pencils to represent
the colour and grain.

2) You can use more than one colour to get the right shade.

3) Wood grain can be added using a darker pencil.
Remember that the side grain and the end grain
look different.

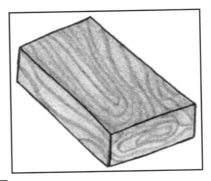

Metal — if it's Shiny, Draw the Reflections...

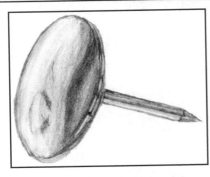

1) Metals can have a variety of colours and finishes.

2) You could have flat sheet metal, or metal with a texture.

3) When shading shiny metal you must be aware of highlights.
Try looking closely at a piece of shiny metal in the light.
What do the reflections actually look like?

4) Textured metal can be represented using line techniques,
e.g. drawing lines to show any ridges, bumps etc.

Plastic — Here's a Few Tricks of the Trade...

1) Marker pens can be used to create the effect of plastic.
Alternatively you could use soft coloured pencils or poster paints.

2) Pale coloured marker pens, watercolour paints or pencils or
coloured pencils can be used to make an object appear transparent.
You may even see objects through the transparent object.

3) Most dark colours look opaque automatically,
but you could make a pale coloured material
look opaque using watercolour paints by adding
a bit of yellow.

Aaahh — look at the pretty pictures...

Once you've got the hang of highlights, don't restrict yourself to only using them on metals.
Anything shiny — glass, smooth plastic or any polished surface — will pick up highlights as well.

Enhancement — Colour and Mood

The use of <u>colour</u> is very important when producing drawings.
As well as being used to make a product <u>aesthetically</u> pleasing, it can be used to <u>represent mood</u>.

Colours can be Organised into Different Groups

1) There are two main types of colour: <u>primary</u> and <u>secondary</u>.

2) The primary colours (<u>red</u>, <u>blue</u> and <u>yellow</u>) can be mixed together to produce <u>any</u> other colour.

3) <u>Secondary colours</u> are colours made by <u>mixing</u> together primary colours.

4) Colour can be represented on a <u>colour wheel</u> which shows you how all the colours fit together.

N.B. This colour wheel only applies to paint or pigments — not to light. The primary colours for light are red, green and blue, which gives a different set of secondary colours as well.

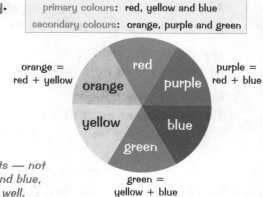

primary colours: red, yellow and blue
secondary colours: orange, purple and green

orange = red + yellow

purple = red + blue

green = yellow + blue

Complementary Colours are on Opposite Sides of the Wheel

1) <u>Complementary</u> or <u>contrasting</u> colours are found <u>opposite</u> each other on the <u>colour wheel</u>.

2) Examples are red and green, blue and orange, yellow and purple.

3) In <u>CAD packages</u> you can <u>select colours</u> and also <u>edit</u> colours to specific requirements.

4) 'Hue' is another word for 'colour'. It's used a lot in drawing software, e.g. CorelDraw, Photoshop.

Colours can be Used to Represent Mood

1) Different colours can represent different <u>moods</u> or <u>feelings</u>.

2) To create a <u>heavy</u> mood, you might use a <u>dark solid colour</u> while for a lighter mood you'd go for a <u>paler colour</u>.

E.g. the Batman cartoon uses very dark colours to give it a sinister feel, whereas the Peanuts cartoon uses light, pastelly colours which gives a happier, less serious feel to the cartoon.

*Mmm...
Nice hot weather...*

BRRR...

3) <u>Hot</u> is usually represented by <u>reds</u> or oranges, whereas <u>blues</u> are normally associated with <u>cold</u>.

4) Colours can also represent the <u>mood</u>. For example <u>green</u> is often associated with <u>calm</u> or <u>relaxation</u>, while <u>red</u> often represents <u>anger</u> and <u>conflict</u>.

With all this green I feel so serene.

Top tip 84: Girl/boyfriend too moody? Just hold up the green card...

Works every time. When they're in a <u>real strop</u> and <u>throwing things</u> at you, just hold up the green card and they'll instantly transform into <u>Snow White</u> or and start singing sweet melodies about birds, daffodils and goats.

Enhancement — Colour in Print

There are two common <u>sets</u> of colours used in print — <u>RGB</u> and <u>CMYK</u>.
They have different uses. Anyway, it's all really really really exciting, so read on...

Traditional Television Screens use Three Basic Colours

1) All pictures on a <u>television screen</u> are made from the colours <u>red</u>, <u>green</u> and <u>blue</u> (RGB colours).

2) The screen is made up of thousands of tiny coloured <u>dots</u> (<u>pixels</u>).

3) Each tiny pixel consists of a <u>red</u>, <u>green</u> and <u>blue</u> bar or dot. The intensity of each of these bars (or dots) produces the final pixel colour you see. It's all <u>dead clever</u>.

Colour Printers use a Different System

1) Colour printers use <u>cyan</u>, <u>magenta</u>, <u>yellow</u> and <u>black</u> (CMYK) as their key colours. *(The 'K' stands for 'key' — it means black.)*

2) Anything that's printed in colour is made up of a <u>mixture</u> of these colours.

3) When the computer is instructed to print, the printer recognises the required colour and adds <u>layers</u> of cyan, magenta, yellow and black to make the final colour.

4) Some PC printers use <u>extra colours</u> as well as CMYK to make the image look more realistic — especially things like flesh tones in photos of people.

5) <u>Newspapers</u> and the like are printed as loads of little <u>dots</u> of colour — usually 150 dpi (dots per inch). You can see them too if you look real close.

You can make black by mixing the other three colours, but using black ink usually looks better, and works out cheaper if you're printing a lot of black.

cyan layer   magenta layer   yellow layer   black layer

Famous photo of a ski-streaker at the 1967 Samurai Games.

Screen Printing uses a Similar System

1) When screen printing you also add colour in <u>layers</u>.

2) These layers build up to produce the final colour.

3) This is the traditional system of colouring <u>paper</u> and <u>cloth</u>.

4) An example of printing using layers is <u>newspapers</u>, where you can often see a colour bar showing the colours used.

The screen is made of a very fine mesh with a stencil on it. The mesh is held taut around a strong wooden frame. To print a design, you lop a load of dye cream onto the mesh, then pull across a rubber squeegee to push the dye through the holes. And you get a pretty pattern on your T-shirt.

Colour me with your kisses baby, colour me with your love...

Or is it cover me? Oh yeah, it is. Well, never mind. Primary colours can be a confusing subject. When you're mixing paints or inks, the primary colours are <u>subtractive</u>. With subtractive colours, if you mix all three you end up with <u>black</u>. Light on the other hand is <u>additive</u> which means mixing them all gives you <u>white</u>. That's what happens in TVs. Confusing, but fascinating don't you think... No?

3

Paper Sizes, Mounting, Fixatives

<u>Paper</u> comes in all different shapes and sizes. You need to learn the <u>standard sizes</u> of paper so that you can talk about them at dinner parties. And at school.

There are Many Standard Paper Sizes

1) Paper sizes go <u>from A0</u> (which has an area of 1 m²) to A1, A2, and so on — halving in size (area) each time.

2) The most common paper sizes used in UK schools are <u>A4</u> and <u>A3</u>. A4 is 297 mm × 210 mm, in case you're interested.

3) Many other sizes are also available:

- <u>A4</u> paper is <u>half</u> the size of <u>A3</u> paper.
- <u>A5</u> paper is <u>half</u> the size of <u>A4</u> paper.
- <u>A6</u> paper is <u>half</u> the size of <u>A5</u> paper.

As the paper gets smaller the number increases.

The width of A3 paper is the length of A4.
The length of A3 paper is double the width of A4.

4) If the page is <u>tall</u>, it's referred to as 'portrait', whereas if it's <u>wide</u>, it's called 'landscape'.

Clever Ben has correctly labelled these sheets of paper. Well done, Ben!

You can Make Booklets from Sheets of Paper

1) <u>Booklets</u> can be made by <u>folding</u> sheets of paper.

2) If <u>A4</u> paper is used and <u>folded in half</u> it creates 4 sides or <u>pages</u> which are <u>A5</u> size.

3) Booklets can be <u>stapled</u> to hold the separate sheets together.

Separate sheets of A4

fold

and staple

Cardboard Mounts can be Made to Frame a Picture

1) You can make a <u>mount</u> to <u>frame</u> your picture using a piece of <u>cardboard</u>.

2) You need to choose an appropriate size of card and cut a hole in the <u>middle</u>.

3) The hole is usually positioned slightly <u>higher</u> than the <u>middle</u> of the picture, to help <u>balance</u> it.

4) Before you frame your picture, it's important to <u>protect</u> it.

5) Using a <u>fixative</u> spray or paint you can protect your picture from <u>smudging</u> or <u>fading</u>.

So A1 are named after a paper size — wow, they are so cool...

Claudia Schiffer asked me out once. She asked me for a piece of A6 paper to write her number on, but I gave her A5 by mistake and she wasn't interested. How I wish I'd known my paper sizes.

CAD/CAM

CAD stands for <u>Computer-Aided Design</u> — it's the process of <u>designing</u> using a <u>computer</u>.
CAM stands for <u>Computer-Aided Manufacture</u> — using <u>machines</u> to make designs created on a computer.

CAD Images can be Changed to Suit the Customers' Needs

1) Using <u>CAD packages</u> you can produce <u>drawings</u> of a <u>concept</u> or product.

2) In order to show <u>specific details</u> the images can be manipulated in a number of ways.

3) You could show details of <u>dimensions</u>, <u>materials</u> or how the final product will appear.

4) This enables the customer to <u>fully understand</u> the designs and specify any changes before manufacturing.

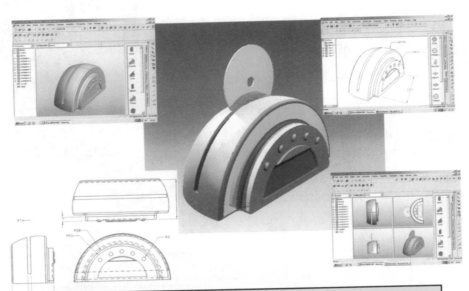

Examples of CAD drawings using Pro/DESKTOP software

Lettering can be Added to Products Using CAD/CAM

1) Lettering varies from <u>ornate, traditional styles</u> to <u>modern, dynamic</u> styles.

2) Different lettering styles (fonts) are used for different <u>purposes</u>.

3) A <u>traditional</u> style wouldn't really be suitable for a <u>trendy</u>, <u>new</u>, <u>up-to-date</u> product.

4) In the same way, very <u>modern</u> styles may look out of place on some <u>greetings cards</u>.

5) Lettering can be created <u>by hand</u> or using <u>CAD</u>.

6) Lettering designed using a <u>CAD package</u> can be sent to a <u>CAM machine</u>, e.g. <u>a vinyl cutter</u>, to be produced.

7) This lets you make a <u>very accurate</u> product.

Font Styles

T serif	T sans serif (without serifs)	$\mathscr{T}$ script
T bold	T light	*T* italic

Can you imagine anything more exciting than a vinyl cutter...

Different fonts really do make a difference to how people see things. This is a very formal font.
This is quite a 'fun' font. This makes me think of gothicy-type things. ☺ ☜ ☹ ☺ ✿ ☞ ♛ ♠ ♪ *

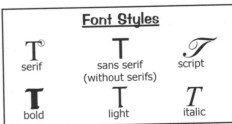

* This says 'jellyfish' in Wingdings.

Protecting Paper Products

Sometimes it's really important to <u>protect</u> photographs, images and graphics to make sure they're <u>not damaged</u> easily.

Paper is *Very* Fragile

1) Paper is <u>easily damaged</u> by water and damp environments.

2) <u>Protecting</u> a paper product can extend its useful life.

3) Examples of products that may need protecting are <u>menus</u>, <u>instruction leaflets</u> and <u>signs</u>.

You can *Cover* the Paper to Form a Layer of *Protection*

1) Paper products can be protected by <u>encapsulating</u> (enclosing) them in <u>sealed pockets</u>.

2) This is done using a <u>laminating machine</u>.

3) The paper product is <u>laid between</u> two sheets of clear plastic.

4) This sandwich is then inserted into the laminating machine, which <u>heats</u> the plastic and <u>seals</u> in the paper.

5) In industry, brochures can be laminated on one or both sides using gloss or matt laminate.

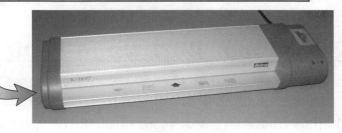

Before   After

It's probably not a good idea to try this with a real sandwich...

For *Security*, Photographs and Names are *Encapsulated*

1) <u>Passports</u>, security <u>identity badges</u> and <u>driving licences</u> use photographs to identify authorised people.

2) A <u>protective</u> film is added in order to ensure that the <u>photos</u> are not <u>damaged</u> or <u>changed</u> in any way.

3) Sometimes items are <u>encapsulated</u> to ensure that components are not <u>lost</u> or <u>damaged</u>, e.g. magazines with inserts sent through the post. This process is known as <u>polywrapping</u>.

Who'd want to laminate a sandwich anyway?...

So, that's "protecting paper products" for you. Nuff said. No? You want me to go on? Oh. Um... OK — top Glastonbury tip: Write your name in big letters on a groovy-coloured bit of paper and laminate it — then stick it onto your tent with masking tape so you can find your tent again.

Recording Stages using Photography

Photographs are an alternative way of recording information about products or images.
They can be used for research purposes or through the designing stage to record developments.

Take Photographs as Primary Evidence

1) You can take photographs to record the original problem.

2) It's worth taking photographs of other things that you'll need to think about during the design process, like the target user.

3) These images can then be stored and used later.

4) If a digital camera is used, the images can be stored on computer and used in presentations and reports.

5) There's also software that lets you play around with digital images to suit individual requirements. For example, colour could be adjusted to show how a product would look with different finishes.

montage of images using Photoshop

Record your Work using Photographs

1) Photographs can be used to record all intermediate stages of the design process, from research through to final outcome and testing.

2) These make a useful record of what's been achieved.

3) The photos can then be used in presentations about the product or to introduce new ideas.

If I had a photograph of you — something to remind me...

...I wouldn't spend my life just wishing... doo doo doodoo doo doo deedoo doo...
Ahem. Sorry, miles away. Yep — digital photos are ace cos you can store them safely on your
PC, then if you pour your cup of tea all over your paper copy, you can just print another one.

Revision Summary

Hello again. It's me, the friendly Revision Summary. You may remember me from such sections as Section One and Section Two. You know why I'm here — do all these questions and find out how much you've learned. You can look back at the relevant bit of the section if you get stuck, but keep doing them till you can answer every single question without looking back.

If you can't do these questions, you don't know everything you need to know. Simple as that.

1) What is a prototype and why are they made?

2) Why is it important to find a 'gap in the market' before designing and launching a new product?

3) Suggest one way that you could attract a potential customer to a new product.

4) What are freehand sketches useful for?

5) How could you draw a simple 3-D sketch?

6) How would you draw a circle or ellipse to the correct proportions when sketching?

7) How and why would you use a grid when sketching?

8) Why might you want to view an object in wireframe?

9) What does the term 'rendering' mean?

10) Give four different shading techniques that you could use to make an object appear 3-D. Draw a cube to illustrate each of these methods.

11) Draw three 3-D shapes and shade them to look like wood, metal and plastic respectively.

12) Draw two 3-D shapes. Shade one to appear transparent and the other opaque.

13) For paints/pigments, what colours are classed as primary colours and which are the secondary colours?

14) What are complementary colours? Give three examples of complementary pairs.

15) What does 'hue' mean?

16) What colour is usually associated with anger and what colour is associated with cold?

17) What colours are used in a television screen? How does each pixel change colour?

18) What colours do colour printers usually use?

19) Give an example of a product that has been printed. How are the colours produced?

20) How big is A3 paper compared to A4 paper?

21) If you were making a booklet by folding A4 paper in half, how big would the booklet be?

22) Explain, using drawings and notes, how you could mount a picture and protect it from smudging.

23) Using CAD to produce designs, what information can you show a client?

24) What style of lettering would be suitable for labels on a trendy new electrical product, e.g. an MP3 player, and how could this lettering be produced using CAD/CAM?

25) How could you protect a photo or image from being damaged in a damp or moist environment?

26) How can photos be used throughout the design process?

Pictorial Drawings

"Pictorial drawings — well, that's just... um... pictures, innit..."
Why, yes, my little pumpkin, but there's more to it than that...

Perspective Drawing — using Vanishing Points

1) <u>Perspective drawing</u> tries to show what something actually looks like — smaller in the distance, larger close to. It does this by using lines that appear to meet at points called <u>vanishing points</u>.

2) These points are in the distance on the <u>horizon line</u>.

3) There are two types of perspective commonly used — <u>one-point</u> and <u>two-point</u> perspective.

One-Point Perspective — for Drawing Objects Head On

1) <u>One-point perspective</u> uses only <u>one vanishing point</u>.

2) The <u>front</u> view of an object is drawn <u>head on</u>.

3) <u>Lines</u> are then drawn to the <u>vanishing point</u> on the <u>horizon line</u>.

  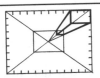

Use a <u>grid</u> to help to draw in proportion.

You've probably seen one-point perspective in cartoons without even realising it...

Two-Point Perspective — for Objects at an Angle

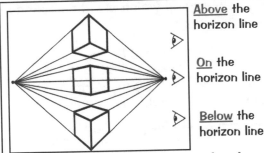

Above the horizon line

On the horizon line

Below the horizon line

The <u>position</u> of the <u>eye level</u> affects how the object appears.

1) <u>Two-point perspective</u> gives a <u>more realistic</u> view of an object drawn <u>at an angle</u>.

2) The <u>horizon line</u> is drawn <u>horizontally</u> across the page.

3) <u>Two vanishing points</u> are marked on the horizon line.

4) The object is drawn by starting with the front edge and then <u>projecting lines</u> to the vanishing points.

5) Remember that <u>vertical lines remain vertical</u> and all <u>horizontal lines go to the vanishing points</u>.

Isometric drawing shows objects at 30°

1) Isometric drawing can be used to show a <u>3-D picture</u> of an object.

2) It <u>doesn't show perspective</u> (things don't get smaller in the distance), but it's easier to get dimensions right than in perspective drawing.

3) There are <u>three main rules</u> when drawing in isometric:

> 1. Vertical lines remain vertical.
> 2. Horizontal lines are drawn at 30°.
> 3. All lines are parallel on regular objects.

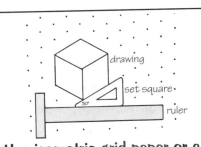
drawing
set square
ruler

Use isometric <u>grid paper</u> or a <u>30°/60° set square</u>.

Perspective drawing? — can't see the point in that...

Bit of a stumper — which to use when... OK, quick summary then: <u>perspective</u> drawing is <u>more realistic</u> (<u>2-pt</u> is more <u>lifelike</u> than 1-pt), but <u>isometric</u> drawing is <u>easier</u> (if you use isometric paper).

Working Drawings

Working drawings are for explaining to a production team how to make a product.
They include details on sizes, materials and assembly. And they'rrre grrreat...

3rd Angle Orthographic Projection (2-D views to you and me)

1) Orthographic projection shows 2-D views of a 3-D object.
2) All details are shown so the product can be made to the designer's requirements.
3) The front view, plan view and end view of the product are drawn accurately to scale.
4) The symbol for 3rd angle orthographic projection is: ⊕ ◁
5) To avoid confusion, lines and dimensions must conform to the following British Standards recommendations:

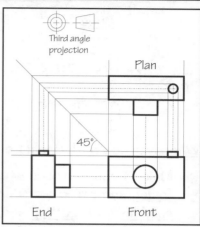
third angle projection of camera

outlines: thick and continuous
projection/construction lines: light and continuous
centre lines: alternate short and long dashes, light
hidden details: short dashes, light
dimension lines: medium and continuous

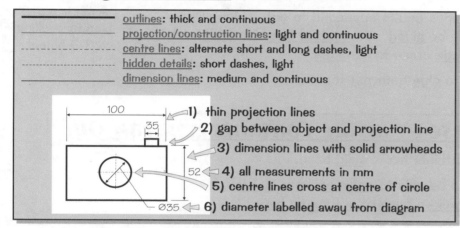

1) thin projection lines
2) gap between object and projection line
3) dimension lines with solid arrowheads
4) all measurements in mm
5) centre lines cross at centre of circle
6) diameter labelled away from diagram

Assembly Drawings show how a Product Fits Together

There are a few ways of showing how things fit together —
exploded drawings and sectional drawings are the important ones.

EXPLODED DRAWINGS
1) You draw the product with each separate part of it moved out as if it's been exploded.
2) Each part of the product is drawn in line with the part it is attached to.
3) Dotted lines show where the part has been exploded from.

SECTIONAL DRAWINGS
1) Sectional drawings show additional details.
2) The product is imagined to be cut in half through section X,Y to draw the internal details.

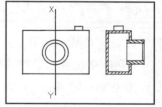

Plan Views Should be Drawn to Scale

1) An area can be drawn to scale to show details of where objects are in relation to each other.
2) They're drawn from above.
3) The scale must be shown clearly as a ratio, e.g. 1:2. With a scale of 1:2 the drawing is half the product's actual size. (And of course 1:1 is full size.)

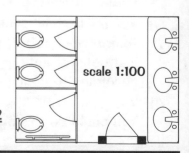
scale 1:100

3rd angle orthographic projection — try saying that 10 times fast...
You need to learn all these details — there's nowt here that you don't need to know. And don't forget to use those British Standards line conventions — might be a pain, but yer stuck with 'em.

Surfaces, Nets and Boxes

You can make any <u>3-D object</u> by producing a <u>2-D pattern</u> (<u>net</u>) which you can fold and glue together. You can either do them by hand (in true Blue Peter fashion) or you can produce them using <u>CAD/CAM</u>.

You Should Know these Nets like the Back of Your Hand...

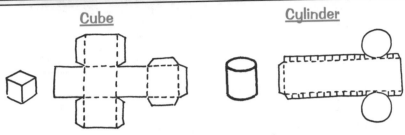

<u>Cube</u>   <u>Cylinder</u>   <u>Triangular-based pyramid</u>

<u>Whenever</u> you're designing a net, <u>remember</u> to:

1) Make it dead obvious which lines you're supposed to <u>cut</u>, which will be <u>folded</u> and which areas are to be <u>glued</u>. Use <u>dotted lines</u> for <u>folds</u> and <u>solid lines</u> for <u>cutting</u> and <u>shade</u> areas to be <u>glued</u>.

2) Always include <u>enough tabs</u> to <u>glue</u> your net together.

> A <u>net</u> is a 2-D plan for making a 3-D object.

Don't Forget the Base — or the Contents will Fall Out

1) It's very important that a container has a <u>solid</u> base.

2) If you want your container to be able to <u>collapse</u> when <u>not in use</u> then you need to include a <u>tuck-in base</u> or <u>automatic base</u>:

1) <u>Tuck-in</u> bases <u>slot into</u> the <u>main part</u> of the box.

2) They often <u>need glue</u> or tape to hold them in place.

1) <u>Automatic</u> bases are <u>formed</u> when the box is <u>constructed</u>.

2) The base is <u>part of</u> the net and <u>no additional glue</u> is needed to ensure it holds firmly.

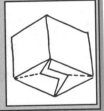

Use CAD/CAM to Make Sure it's Accurate

1) Using CAD/CAM (see pages 32 & 51-52) is an ideal way to <u>make sure</u> your net is <u>cut out accurately</u>.

2) You could design your net on a <u>computer</u> using <u>2-D design software</u>.

3) You could then send it to a <u>CAM</u> machine (e.g. a vinyl cutter) which will follow your instructions and <u>cut out</u> or <u>score lines</u> according to your design.

4) You need to tell the CAM machine <u>which lines to cut</u> and <u>which to score</u>. You could do this by <u>colour coding</u> your lines to indicate the <u>depth of cut</u> needed.

Base — how low can you go...

Remember — <u>dotted lines</u> for <u>folds</u>, <u>solid lines</u> for <u>cutting</u> and <u>shade in</u> your tabs — then there's no room for confusion. Got that? Smashing.

Graphs and Charts

Aaaaah, and you thought you'd only have to bother with these in Maths... how wrong you were...
Any information you collect from a survey or whatever needs to be communicated somehow.
Graphs and charts are a nice easy way of making your raw data understandable. Learn and grin.

Bar Charts use Bars to Represent Information *(no, really?)*

1) 2-D bar charts can be drawn horizontally or vertically.

2) The information is shown by a series of equally spaced bars of equal width.

3) In this bar chart, different colours are represented by each column.
It clearly shows that more people like the colour blue than red or yellow.

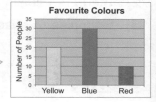

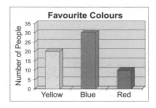

4) Data can also be displayed in 3-D bar charts.
They're just the same, except the bars look solid.

5) They take the form of simple columns drawn using a
particular drawing technique, often oblique.

Pictographs are Graphs made of Pictures

1) Pictographs use symbols or simple pictures to represent information.

2) They make otherwise uninteresting information look more interesting.

3) They're also called pictograms by some people.

Month	Hours of Sunshine
October	☼ ☼ ☼ ☼
November	☼ ☼ ☼
December	☼ ☼
January	☼ ☼
February	☼ ☼
March	☼ ☼ ☼ ☼ ☼

☼ represents 2 hours of sunshine per day

Pie Charts show Proportions *(and they look like Pies)*

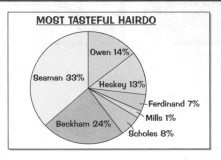

1) Pie charts represent data by dividing a
pie or circle into appropriate portions.

2) Each portion of the pie represents a
certain category.

3) Pie charts are based on percentages
with the whole pie adding up to 100%.

Line Graphs are for Continuous Data, like Time

1) As with bar charts, line graphs show the relationship
between two factors, e.g. speed and time.

2) In line graphs you plot the information on
the graph and draw a line joining the points.

3) These are pretty handy for spotting trends
over time, and also for spotting "blips".

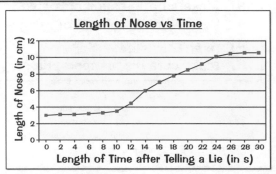

Ah, seen this all before — it's well chart-ered territory...

And time... goes by... so slowly... And time can mean so much...
when shown correctly using an appropriately chosen and labelled graphical representation.

Labels, Icons and Ideograms

Labels... ah yes, labels. Everyone's seen labels before. Don't tell me you never bought a bag *just* because it had a Nike (or whatever) label on it.

Enactive Labels show How to Do Something

1) Enactive labels are used to show how to operate a product.
2) They are usually universally recognised and don't include words.
3) Examples of enactive labels are the control buttons on a stereo:

Iconic Labels — Simple and Easily Recognised

1) Examples of iconic labels appear on your computer screen as shortcuts to software, files or program tools.

2) Icons that identify functions (e.g. the text tool) are similar in all software packages, to help a user to quickly learn how to use new software.

3) Icons are usually little, and immediately recognisable to the user.

And don't forget good old sportswear labelling — people will spend a lot of money just to have that icon stuck on their chest.

Ideograms use Pictures to Represent Ideas

1) Ideograms (pictograms) can be substituted for writing — they're kind of a universal language.
2) They're images that are easily and immediately identifiable.
3) You'll have seen plenty of ideograms in everyday life — e.g. if you go on holiday, you might see a sign with an aeroplane to identify an airport, or one with a telephone receiver pointing to a payphone.

Non-Standard Symbols can be Created

1) If a label doesn't already exist for an object, you can create one.
2) These rules are useful when designing your own label or icon:

> 1) Try not to use any words, so it can be used in any country.
> 2) Make sure the symbol's relevant to the object you're labelling.
> 3) Make sure the symbol is able to be reproduced if it's going to be used on a number of items.
> 4) Keep it simple.
> 5) Make sure it's an appropriate colour.

In most cases people don't consciously think about the colour — they might just instinctively associate a particular colour with a feeling — like red for danger.

> There are some standard colouring conventions that it's worth considering — such as:
>
> 1) Red for STOP or warning
> 2) Green for GO or OK or for something environmentally friendly or vegetarian

Universal language — mgrbli blforg ma pwtr!... hahaha...

Well, quite. Words'd never work if you wanted everyone in the world to understand.

Whereas a picture like this on a gate ⚠ is clearly telling you not to go in there or you'll die.

Branding

Unless you've been living on Jupiter for a couple of decades,
this is a subject you'll be totally familar with.

Graphics Are Everywhere — Promoting Brands

Graphics (i.e. words, pictures and symbols) are applied to a wide range of products in
lots of different situations. On the average high street you can see loads of examples
of logos, trademarks, corporate imagery and visual advertising, etc.

You'll see them on:

1) shopfronts and shop signs,
2) delivery vehicles,
3) shopping bags,
4) confectionery and fast-food packaging,
5) workers' equipment and uniforms,
6) stationery,
7) static advertisements e.g. billboards,
8) mobile advertisements e.g. on buses,
9) branded clothing worn by members of
   the public.

Strong Corporate Identity means Good Brand Recognition

1) Many companies have a corporate look or identity — they
   apply their logo and colour scheme to all printed material
   (e.g. business cards, letterheads and compliments slips) —
   as well as their products, packaging, uniforms and transport.

The new CGP clothing
range — available in the
high street soon.

2) Companies like Body Shop, MacDonald's and Nike have
   very strong corporate identities. Most people can
   recognise each company from its colours or logo alone,
   without the need for words. This is great for the company.

3) The most successful corporate images/colours are those
   which are flexible enough to be applied to different surfaces
   whilst still retaining their impact and recognisability.

Branding irons — now, they're hot...

With branding graphics, the simple, unfussy designs are most effective. Remember, good brand
graphics need to be versatile. For example, you might need transfers, stickers, embroidered
patches, and all sorts of things to get your design onto all the necessary surfaces.

Flow Charts and Sequential Illustrations

Flow charts show the stages of an operation clearly by breaking them down into little chunks.

A Flow Chart Shows Events in the Order they Happen

1) A flow chart is a diagram which shows a number of events in the order that they take place.
2) Each event has a symbol (a shaped box).
3) Different symbols show different types of event, e.g. decisions or operations.
4) Inside each symbol is something that explains what is happening at that stage. It could be a word, a few words, a photograph or a drawing.

Flow Charts use Standard Symbols

1) At the beginning or the end of a flow chart there is always a sausage shape.

2) Operations or processes are represented by rectangles.

3) Questions or decisions are represented by rhombuses (diamond shapes).

4) Arrows are drawn between each event to show the flow and the direction of the flow.

You don't need to break everything up into little pieces...

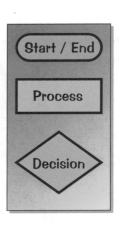

Flow chart for crossing a road:

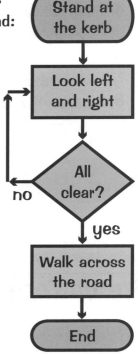

You can Also use Sequential Illustrations

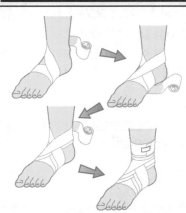

1) Instead of producing a flow chart, you can use a series of illustrations to show how to do something.

2) You'll see examples of this when you buy flat-pack furniture — it comes with simple instructions that show how to build it.

3) These instructions use pictures and very few words so that everybody should be able to follow them.

Just go with the flow, man...

Yeah man, don't let this revision lark get too heavy, man. If it all gets too much, you can always make a chart to help you organise. Where would we be without charts. Charts, man... like... cool.

Revision Summary

Congratulations! You've completed the section on drawing techniques and now know everything from drawing in 3-D to writing using pictures instead of words. Now here's the test. You should find the next few questions a doddle, so have a go and see how you get on. If you get any wrong have a quick look back and try again. After all, they do say "Practice makes perfect"...

1) Name two 3-D drawing techniques.

2) In perspective drawing, what is a vanishing point?

3) In perspective drawing, what do we mean by the horizon line?

4) When should you use each type of perspective drawing?

5) What angle is an object drawn at in an isometric drawing?

6) What is the symbol for 3rd angle orthographic projection?

7) What three views are drawn when completing a 3rd angle orthographic projection of an object?

8) Draw an exploded drawing of a toy car.

9) Why might you draw a sectional drawing of an object?

10) How can you make a 3-D object using a sheet of cardboard?

11) What do you need to consider when designing a net?

12) What is an automatic base?

13) How could you use CAD/CAM to cut out your shape net?

14) What is a bar chart? What is a 3-D bar chart?

15) What is the difference between a bar chart and a pictograph? Why might you draw a pictograph rather than a bar chart?

16) What is a pie chart? What percentage does a full pie chart add up to?

17) What is an enactive label? Draw the enactive labels that you'd expect to find on a stereo.

18) Write down five rules to remember when designing your own non-standard symbol.

19) How could colour be used in designing labels?

20) Why are ideograms/pictograms more suitable for use around the world than labels containing words or numbers?

21) What is a flow chart? How are they used to show clearly a process from start to finish?

22) What are the correct symbols for the beginning/end, processes and decisions on flow charts?

23) Produce some assembly instructions for assembling a flat-pack unit with three shelves that fix together with screws onto two outside panels, as shown below.

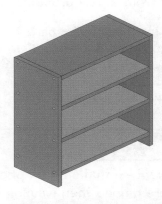

Why People Buy a Product

If you know what makes people buy things, it becomes <u>easier</u> to design stuff they'll want.
So for a designer, finding out this information is dead important.

Good Design and Good Manufacture are Different Things

A well-designed product:

- has the potential to carry out its <u>function</u> really well —
  because the <u>thinking</u> that's gone into the design is good,
- <u>looks</u> good and attracts consumers.

A well-manufactured product:

- has been <u>made</u> to a <u>good standard</u> — things like the
  finish, folds, colour and material are all satisfactory,
- is <u>accurate</u> to the original design.

Customers Choose Products for Different Reasons

Not everyone buys a product for the same reasons. People might buy something because of:

`COST` Customers might think the product is good <u>value for money</u>.

`BRAND LOYALTY` Customers might be <u>loyal</u> to a company after finding previous goods to be good quality.

`AESTHETIC APPEAL` Customers might like the <u>look</u> and <u>design</u> of the product.

`ADVERTISING` This raises <u>product awareness</u>, and can make customers more likely to buy a product.

`FASHION` Some customers will be more likely to buy something they think is <u>up to date</u> and <u>trendy</u>.

Manufacturers Survey Current Market Trends

It's important for manufacturers to know what <u>consumers think</u> of their product. In order to
improve their product they have to keep up with <u>current trends</u> in the market. They have to know:

- what colours, materials and styles are <u>fashionable</u>,
- if consumers like the <u>design</u> and <u>quality</u> of their product,
- if consumers like their <u>advertising</u>,
- how much <u>money</u> consumers are willing to pay for the product.

See page 46 for more on how manufacturers can find this stuff out.

Manufacturers also Need Certain Things from a Product

<u>Manufacturers</u> will have opinions on what makes for a 'good' product. Manufacturers often work
out a set of <u>criteria</u> stating what they want from a new product. They might require that:

1) the time taken to manufacture and assemble the different parts of the product is reasonably fast,
2) the materials and equipment used to manufacture the product are easy to obtain and cost-effective,
3) the product meets a need — consumers will find it useful,
4) the product carries out its function well — it has been designed and manufactured to a high standard,
5) the product looks good and will be attractive to consumers.

Why buy it? Because it's there...

People are more likely to buy things they want — that's no surprise. But being able to decide <u>what</u>
consumers want and <u>why</u> can be worth more money than winning the Lottery. So it's important.

Evaluation

Even <u>after</u> a product's been manufactured, the design process doesn't really <u>stop</u>. In industry, the process of evaluation and improvement is <u>ongoing</u>.

The <u>Finished Product</u> Needs to be Evaluated

1) Once a product has been finished, its <u>strengths</u> and <u>weaknesses</u> need to be assessed.

2) This is so that <u>lessons</u> can be learnt for <u>future</u> products. For example, are any <u>safety modifications</u> necessary, or could any <u>improvements</u> be made?

3) Similarly, it's important to record any <u>problems</u> that were encountered and how they were <u>overcome</u>. This goes for both the <u>design</u> and <u>manufacturing</u> stages. It might help avoid similar problems next time.

4) It's important to get <u>other people's</u> opinions as well when it comes to evaluating a product — ask <u>potential users</u> and <u>experts</u> who have designed this kind of product before (see next page for more on this).

Good points	Bad points

Quality Control

Part of the ongoing evaluation process is to monitor quality all the time the product is being manufactured. <u>Checks</u> need to be made at various stages of the manufacturing process to make sure the product is being produced to the <u>highest</u> possible <u>standard</u>.

<u>Records</u> of Everything are Kept from the <u>Very Start</u>

1) From the very first moment of the design process, <u>records</u> of <u>ideas</u>, <u>prototypes</u>, <u>experiments</u>, etc. are kept.

2) These records can be in the form of <u>written notes</u>, <u>data</u> from experiments, <u>videos</u> of prototypes being tested, and so on.

3) This makes it easy to see <u>why</u> certain ideas were <u>dropped</u> and why others were <u>persevered</u> with.

4) It might sometimes be necessary to go back to an earlier idea, and this is made much <u>easier</u> if proper records have been kept.

Why Evaluations are <u>Important</u>

1) Designers are always looking at ways to <u>improve</u> their designs.
2) Companies employ designers to make use of the <u>latest innovations</u> in technology.
3) If designers were always <u>happy</u> with how things were, we wouldn't have seen the innovations in technology that we all take for granted.

Unless designers can be <u>critical</u> of their designs in a constructive way:
1) Their designs would <u>never improve</u>.
2) Products would <u>fail to keep up</u> with the latest trends and fashions.

My product's ready-recycled — it's a load of rubbish...

Don't underestimate how important an evaluation of a finished product is. If you don't improve upon your product, someone else will. Oh yes, it's a cut-throat world out there. It's dog eat dog, survival of the fittest, and so on and so on. Evaluations are important, and don't you forget it.

Evaluation

There are <u>various</u> ways to evaluate a product. The <u>designers</u> have a big role to play in any evaluation, but so do the people who will actually <u>use</u> the product.

Comment on the Success of your Final Design

The most obvious way to evaluate a finished product is to compare it against its original <u>design specification</u>. But there are other measures of success as well, such as:

FUNCTION — How well does the final design meet the intended task — <u>does it work</u>?

TIMESCALE — Did you complete the task <u>on time</u>?
Did some things take <u>more/less</u> time to complete than others?

SAFETY — Is the design <u>safe</u>? Were all <u>safety precautions</u> taken during making?

COST — Has the design been made within the original <u>budget</u>?

ERGONOMICS — Is the design <u>practical</u> — could the majority of people use it?

MATERIALS — Were the materials used the <u>right</u> ones to use?
If not, suggest what materials could have been used and <u>why</u>.

AESTHETICS — Comment on the <u>visual</u> success of the product.
Mention its colour, shape, layout, visual impact, size (and you could also mention its texture and feel while you're doing this kind of thing).

ENVIRONMENTAL — Did you make good use of materials and resources?
Could there have been <u>less waste</u> generated?

Talk to your Target Audience

It's also important to ask the intended users of a product what they think of it.
Things to find out might include:

1) Is the product <u>easy to use</u>?
2) Is it <u>well made</u>?
3) Is it easy to <u>maintain</u>?
4) Does it look <u>attractive</u>?

Get Opinions using Questionnaires and Focus Groups

Manufacturers can get information from consumers in different ways, for example:

QUESTIONNAIRES — These ask a series of <u>questions</u> about consumer habits and <u>preferences</u>. A <u>large number</u> and <u>variety</u> of people can be targeted with a questionnaire.

FOCUS GROUPS — In these a <u>small group</u> of consumers are encouraged to discuss their <u>opinions</u> about the product in detail.

I get opinions from Charley — he's got an opinion on everything...

Questionnaires and focus groups — phew, what a barrel of laughs they are. But they are important. Questionnaires are great for collecting data about <u>how many</u> people think this or that, whereas focus groups are better for finding out <u>why</u> they think as they do.

Moral and Cultural Issues

It's no good designing the best pair of <u>pants</u> ever if no one will wear them because the design is offensive in some way. You need to be sensitive and avoid offending people unnecessarily.

Design must be Socially and Environmentally Responsible

When you're selecting <u>materials</u>, <u>components</u> and <u>manufacturing processes</u>, you need to consider:

1) whether <u>using the product</u> might <u>harm</u> people or the environment (this includes finding out whether any <u>materials</u> used, including paints and varnishes, are <u>toxic)</u>,

2) whether the <u>manufacture</u> of the product harms people, e.g. through dangerous <u>working conditions</u> for manufacturing workers, or because components are produced using <u>child labour</u>,

3) whether the <u>manufacture</u> of the product harms the environment, e.g. consider how much <u>waste material</u> will be produced, and how it's going to be disposed of,

4) whether <u>recycled materials</u> could be used to manufacture the product or its packaging,

5) whether <u>biodegradable or recyclable</u> materials could be used (especially if the product's designed to be <u>thrown away</u> after use).

Be Aware of the Feelings of Others

You'll need to exercise a little sensitivity when you're designing stuff...

1) Designers need to be <u>sensitive</u> to the feelings of different groups in society.

2) Make sure that your design does not <u>put off</u>, <u>insult</u> or <u>offend</u> people for <u>political</u>, <u>religious</u>, <u>gender</u> or <u>cultural</u> reasons.

3) Certain <u>symbols</u> are almost certain to offend some people no matter how they're used, e.g. a swastika.

4) Other symbolism will offend people if they believe it's been <u>misused</u> or <u>abused</u>. This is especially true for religious symbols.

5) But it's not only abuse of religious symbols which can cause offence. Other <u>images</u>, <u>colours</u> and <u>styles</u> can easily put people from certain cultures off a product.

6) Some things might not be obvious at all — for instance, <u>certain colours</u> are seen as good or bad luck in some cultures.

This sort of thing might have appeared in the 1920s...

...but you wouldn't get away with it today.

7) More obvious examples include <u>nudity</u> and <u>violence</u>. Although images containing nudity or violence won't offend everyone, it's very possible that you will end up offending some people.

8) It's impossible to list <u>everything</u> that could cause offence. You just have to try and put yourself in other people's shoes, and use a little <u>imagination</u> to guess how they might feel when they see your design.

Watch what you're saying — better sensitive than sorry...

Designers have got to think about this sort of stuff nowadays, since consumers pay more attention to the way products have been made. It's a good thing, since it eases environmental problems — and means people are less likely to be exploited by being paid poor wages, etc.

Section Five — The Wider World

Environmental Issues

We live in a consumer culture where everyone wants to <u>own</u> and <u>upgrade</u> their possessions. This is all well and good, but the consequences for the <u>environment</u> can be pretty severe.

Manufacturing Products Causes Environmental Problems

1) The <u>rainforests</u> are a prime example of a <u>threatened resource</u>. They produce valuable and exotic <u>hardwoods</u> which are (mostly) <u>not being replaced</u>. There are <u>sustainable</u> hardwood plantations in some countries, but it <u>costs money</u> to organise them and check that they're all above board.

2) <u>Softwoods</u> (which can regenerate themselves in a person's lifetime) are a <u>greener choice</u>, as are <u>recycled</u> materials that <u>use waste wood</u>, e.g. chipboard.

3) However, <u>single-species plantations</u> aren't ideal — they're unable to <u>support</u> many other animal and plant species, leading to a reduction in <u>biodiversity</u>.

4) It isn't just trees that we need to worry about, however. <u>Metal ores</u> are taken from the Earth's crust, and there's only a <u>limited amount</u> of each ore.

5) Also, most <u>plastics</u> come from <u>oil</u>, which will eventually <u>run out</u>.

Throwing Away Old Products Causes Pollution

1) At the end of its life, an old product needs to be <u>disposed of</u> to make way for a shiny new one. Most waste goes into <u>landfill</u>. Some chemicals used in products cause <u>serious problems</u> when they get into watercourses or into the soil. There are <u>laws</u> about what can be dumped into landfill sites and what has to be <u>recycled</u> or <u>specially treated</u> to make it <u>safe</u>.

2) <u>Packaging</u> (see page 64) contributes to the problem of waste. Designers need to assess <u>how much</u> packaging is actually <u>needed</u> for a product, and how it will be <u>disposed of</u> or <u>recycled</u>.

Recycling can Help

1) Reusing or recycling products can save <u>money</u> and <u>energy</u>, and help protect the <u>environment</u>.

2) <u>Glass</u> is the most widely used recycled material, but there are plenty of others, e.g. paper, aluminium and some plastics.

3) Some containers (like those for washing-up liquid, fabric conditioners, etc.) are <u>refillable</u>. <u>Refilling</u> used containers is even <u>better</u> than recycling them.

4) The '<u>Möbius Loop</u>' means that the product can be <u>recycled</u>, or that it contains some recyclable material. (The three arrows symbolise the 3 Rs — see page 64.)

5) The '<u>Green Dot</u>' (<u>der Grüne Punkt</u>) shows that the packaging supplier has <u>contributed</u> to the <u>cost</u> of <u>recycling</u> or <u>recovering</u> the material used — it doesn't necessarily mean that the packaging is recyclable.

Paper that's been printed on can be recycled, but the ink content means recycled paper is <u>darker</u> in colour or has a <u>speckled</u> appearance. (It wouldn't be environmentally friendly to <u>bleach</u> it white again.)

Recycling isn't all plain sailing — it can be <u>more expensive</u> to <u>recycle old</u> materials than to <u>use new</u>. Also, <u>environmentally unfriendly by-products</u> can be produced in the recycling process, which kinda defeats the point a bit.

And supermarkets STILL insist on giving me at least 10 new bags for my food...*

In the past, not as many people either knew or cared about the damage that industry and modern living does to the environment. Now we're better informed and more aware — and we're finding that there are loads of things we can do to reduce the effects of our consumer culture.

Section Five — The Wider World

*even though I <u>always</u> take my rucksack, which has <u>plenty</u> of room for <u>all</u> my shopping — grrr...

Legal Issues

You need to be aware of the different rules and regulations regarding design — if you don't know about these you could find yourself in trouble...

Trademarks and Patents Stop People Stealing Ideas

1) The aim of using trademarks is to stop people from selling <u>copies</u> of <u>well-known brands</u>.

2) Individuals or companies or can register <u>trademarks</u> with the <u>Patent Office</u>. Trademarks are <u>distinctive</u> logos, words or pictures that identify a particular company or product. If someone else then uses your trademark (or something <u>similar</u>), you can <u>sue</u> them.

3) <u>Patents</u> are granted when something new has been <u>invented</u>. They allow the inventor (for a <u>limited time</u>) to stop others from making, using or selling the invention <u>without permission</u>.

4) For a patent to be granted, the invention must involve an '<u>inventive step</u>' (you won't get a patent for something that's dead obvious), and must be capable of '<u>industrial application</u>' (so you won't get a patent for a nice painting you've done).

Other Legislation Protects Consumers and Workers

1) <u>The Trade Descriptions Act</u> (1968) applies to all goods. If you're going to be selling anything, you have to be truthful in the way you describe it. This will be important when it comes to making packaging for your product, or advertising it.

2) <u>COSHH</u> stands for the <u>Containment of Substances Hazardous to Health</u>. The COSHH regulations were introduced in <u>1988</u> to protect people from the effects of <u>hazardous substances</u>, <u>materials</u> and <u>processes</u>.

Products can be Labelled if they Meet certain Standards

1) There are various <u>institutes</u> that set <u>standards</u> for certain types of product. These standards are usually concerned with <u>safety</u>, <u>quality</u> or <u>design</u>.

2) Products that meet these standards can usually be <u>labelled</u> to show this (see page 50).

3) It can be <u>important</u> for a manufacturer's products to meet these standards, as many <u>consumers</u> are more willing to buy '<u>approved</u>' products.

4) The <u>British Standards Institute (BSI)</u> is one example of this kind of standards institute. Products that meet its standards may display its 'Kitemark' (see page 50).

5) The <u>International Standards Organisation</u> (<u>ISO</u>) also issues <u>certificates</u> to organisations that meet international standards of quality.

> Other examples of these awarding bodies include:
> i)   the <u>British Electrotechnical Approvals Board</u> (BEAB),
> ii) the <u>British Toy and Hobby Manufacturers' Association</u> (BTMA).

6) And if certain products are going to be sold within the <u>European Union</u> (<u>EU</u>), then they have to be '<u>CE marked</u>'. The CE mark shows that the product has met <u>standards</u> set by the EU.

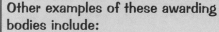

My COSHH — I can't believe there are so many rules...

If you have a brilliant idea that you reckon is going to make your fortune, then my advice would be to get a patent. That way, you can be sure that you'll get the money that your invention surely deserves. And if your invention meets all the relevant standards, then so much the better.

Labels

Manufacturers are legally obliged to put certain information on packaging, and they're responsible for making sure that it's all true. Anyway, I'll let you get on with the page now...

Manufacturers Must Label their Products Carefully

There are various laws in the UK which describe what information labels on products must give, and protect consumers against dishonest labelling. For example:

1) Trade Descriptions Act (1968) — see page 49,
2) Food Labelling Regulations (1996) — these state what information must be on food packaging,
3) Food Safety Act (1990) — this says that food must be correctly described.

Labels can Give Information about Safety

1) Certain institutes allow manufacturers to label their products with special labels if certain standards have been met (see page 49).

2) Labels also help consumers use and maintain a product.

3) They can give useful safety instructions, such as, "This way up", "Ensure catch is fully locked before use" or "Danger — this part gets hot during use".

4) Or they can give maintenance instructions such as, "Clean with warm water only", "Do not use abrasives", "Oil frequently" or "Do not immerse in water".

The British Standards Kitemark

Food Labels Have to Tell You Certain Information

The Food Labelling Regulations state that labels on processed foods must give this information:

1) The name of the product and what it is.

2) What ingredients the product contains, in descending order of weight — preservatives, colourants, emulsifiers and other additives must also be listed (but not flavourings).

3) The name and address of the manufacturer, as well as the country of origin of the ingredients (if from a single country).

4) How the product should be stored.

5) The weight or volume of the product.

6) A best-before or use-by date.

7) Instructions for preparation and cooking (if necessary).

8) Whether a product contains genetically modified ingredients (if greater than 1%).

Nutritional Information Sometimes has to be Included

NUTRITIONAL INFORMATION		
	per 100g	per 55g serving
Energy	2180kJ/525 kcal	1199kJ/289 kcal
Protein	6.5g	3.6g
Carbohydrate	50.0g	27.5g
of which sugars	2.0g	1.1g
Fat	33.0g	18.2g
of which saturates	15.0g	8.3g
Sodium	0.7g	0.4g
Fibre	4.0g	2.2g

- If a special nutritional claim has been made (e.g. 'low sugar') then products must, by law, show the nutritional information.
- This information is often shown in the form of a table.
- It usually shows energy values, protein, carbohydrate, fat, fibre and sodium per 100g and per portion.

Safety Warning: Do not attempt to use this muffin as a parachute...

Although reading this page and learning what's on it may make you want to pull out your own eyeballs, worry not. It's only a page long and once you've learnt it all you can go and take a well-deserved 5-minute break. It's important stuff, so learn it well.

CAD — Computer-Aided Design

CAD is used in the design of many everyday products — from cars through to those little plastic things on springs you put on the end of pencils that you always get in Christmas crackers.

Computer-Aided Design (CAD) — for Plans and Models

CAD is design using computer drawing and modelling packages such as Pro/DESKTOP and Techsoft 2D. They are used by architects, designers and engineers to produce detailed plans, drawings and product simulations. CAD is fast becoming a major part of D&T project work.

Learn these Advantages of CAD

1) Designs can be re-sized (up or down) easily.
2) Designs can be modified quickly and easily without the need for the whole drawing to be done again.
3) It can save costly office space as drawings are stored on hard drives and compact disks instead of bulky plan chests.
4) It can save time and labour and is therefore cost-effective.
5) Designing using CAD can be done on a laptop computer — at home, on the train, etc.
6) Designs can be sent directly and instantly to a client or manufacturer by ISDN or e-mail.
7) Designs and drawings can be in 3-D as well as 2-D and can be viewed from any angle. Also, scales of components in relation to each other can be worked out.

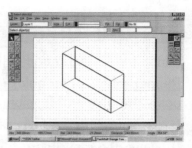

This is "Techsoft Design Tools — 2D design".
(Nice purple background...)

8) Objects drawn with CAD packages can be presented as wireframe models or solid models. They can even be rendered to look like plastic or glass, etc. for customer presentations and 'virtual prototyping'.
9) CAD can be used to create tests and simulations of how a product or material will perform in a given situation without the need to build expensive testing rigs or full-scale prototypes.

CAD has Disadvantages too

1) The initial outlay on software and hardware is high.
2) Expensive and lengthy training is required for best results. Not just any random person off the street can walk into a studio and start designing stuff.
3) Viruses, corrupt files and power cuts can interrupt and destroy work, just like with all IT-based work.
4) Traditional skills and processes may become obsolete, and jobs may be lost. But let's face it, who needs arrow-fletchers and spinning wheel technicians these days...

Shameless love rat — or IT-facilitated design...

When using a CAD package, save your work regularly in case of power loss or crashing computers. Basic computer common sense, but it's easy to forget once you're well stuck in.

CAM — Computer-Aided Manufacture

CAD is clever, but CAM is really clever. That's what I reckon, anyway.
This is all dead important in industry, and is becoming more important in D&T projects as well.

Computer-Aided Manufacture (CAM) — for Making Stuff

1) Computer-Aided Manufacture is the process of <u>manufacturing</u> goods using <u>information received from a CAD package</u>.

2) Data from CAD software is <u>downloaded</u> into the <u>control unit</u> of a manufacturing machine.

3) Components and products are then made on <u>machines</u> (such as <u>milling machines</u>) which are controlled and operated by <u>computers</u> rather than by a person.

4) Popular makes of CAM machines used in schools include: Boxford, Denford, Unimatics and Roland.

Learn the Advantages of CAM

1) Minor (or major) <u>modifications</u> can easily be made <u>without</u> expensive retooling costs.

2) <u>Repeat jobs</u> can be <u>quickly</u> downloaded and set up — making small <u>batch-produced</u> items <u>cost-effective</u> and <u>feasible</u>.

3) It can <u>save</u> time and labour and <u>reduce</u> errors — again making it more cost-effective.

4) It allows the manufacture of products in situations which may be <u>harmful</u> to humans.

5) Machines can do <u>more complex</u> jobs <u>more accurately</u> and in <u>less time</u>.

6) Machines do not need to <u>rest</u>, so <u>productivity</u> is increased.

But there are some Disadvantages too

They're pretty much <u>the same</u> as the <u>disadvantages of CAD</u> on the previous page. It all comes down to <u>man versus machine</u>, really.

Machines used in CAM are Computer Numerically Controlled — CNC

1) The machines used in the CAM process are <u>Computer Numerically Controlled</u>.

2) This means the CAD/CAM program works out the necessary <u>movements</u> of the <u>tool head</u> and <u>sends the data</u> to the machine in the form of numbers. The machine's <u>onboard processor</u> interprets the numbers and controls the movement of the tool head.

3) Machines which can be controlled in this way include <u>lathes</u>, <u>milling</u> machines, <u>drilling</u> machines and <u>flame cutters</u>.

the CAMMI — a CNC cutter and plotter

ADVANTAGES of CNC:

1) <u>Less cost</u> due to less need for separate specialised machine tools for each product.
2) <u>Less</u> chance of human <u>error</u>.
3) The product can <u>easily</u> and quickly be <u>changed</u> without expensive retooling.

DISADVANTAGES of CNC:

1) <u>High initial cost</u> of the machines.
2) <u>High cost of training</u> programmers and operators.
3) Fast <u>special purpose machines</u> are <u>cheaper</u> than CNC machines for large-scale production runs.

My sister's pants were manufactured by a computer — they're CAMiknickers...

Now that people can use CAD/CAM to design things really quickly, it means that they can let their imaginations run wild. There's nothing to lose by trying out lots of different designs on-screen.

DTP and Photo-Editing Software

DTP stands for Desktop Publishing. It's a way of laying out a publication using a computer, rather than doing it all by hand. *(See page 22 for more info.)*

There are Loads of Reasons for Using DTP

1) It saves <u>time</u> and <u>money</u>, since designers can see exactly what a layout will look like before spending money making a colour printed proof.
2) Text and graphics can be <u>arranged anywhere</u> on the page.
3) Designers can <u>experiment</u> more and create more <u>complex</u> designs.
4) Fonts can be easily <u>resized</u> on screen.
5) Scanned <u>images</u> can be <u>imported</u> and incorporated into a design.
6) Designs can be <u>stored</u>, <u>edited</u> and <u>updated</u>.
7) Designs can go <u>directly to press</u> digitally, without loss of quality.
8) Photographs and drawings can be <u>sized</u> and <u>cropped</u> — giving the designer more <u>flexibility</u>.

<u>Microsoft Publisher</u>, <u>QuarkXpress</u> and <u>Adobe Pagemaker</u> are examples of DTP programs.

Graphics Spice up a Page

Graphics can make a printed page <u>look nice</u>, and they can also help you get your point across.

It's all very well wanting <u>graphics</u> on your page, but you have to <u>input</u> the <u>image</u> into the computer first. These are the three main ways:

(1) Use a scanner (2) Use a digital camera (3) Use clipart

Once your image is in the computer, you might want to change it a bit...

1) <u>Adobe Photoshop</u> and <u>Corel Photo-paint</u> are two examples of photo-editing software — they can be used to <u>retouch</u> and <u>manipulate</u> digital images.
2) Images are stored as thousands of dots called <u>pixels</u>. If you zoom in close enough, you can see the individual pixels.
3) Information about the colour of each <u>individual</u> pixel has to be stored, so this kind of image can take up <u>lots of memory</u>.

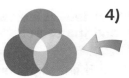

4) Information on computer screens is displayed using just <u>red</u>, <u>green</u> and <u>blue</u> — <u>RGB</u>. By combining these three colours, every other colour can be displayed. (This is also how a **TV** works.)
5) However, images are usually converted to <u>cyan</u>, <u>magenta</u>, <u>yellow</u>, and <u>black</u> (<u>CMYK</u>) for printing (see p30). Each of these colours is printed on paper separately, with the black being applied last.

'K' stands for 'key', but it means 'black'.

I've had enough of graphics — they're driving me dotty...

Designers retouch photographs to make things look as perfect as possible — so you'll never see a photograph of a model in a magazine with a big spot. It's good to experiment with this kind of software — you'll find you can create loads of different visual effects once you get the hang of it.

ICT in Industry

Computers are everywhere these days... everywhere, I tell you...

Increased Use of ICT has Good and Bad Effects

ICT is used more and more in offices, schools, homes, shops, banks... well, pretty much everywhere. People at work, and particularly those in office jobs, have to spend more and more time using computers. This has pros and cons:

PROS

1) Employers benefit because computers can increase the amount of work done. This makes businesses more productive, and so more competitive.
2) Workers benefit if computers can do boring, repetitive tasks and leave them to do the interesting jobs.
3) Transferring data electronically is quick and convenient.
4) The Internet is really useful as a research tool.

CONS

1) It's expensive to keep investing in the latest and most efficient technology, and it takes time and money to retrain staff.
2) There may be job losses as computers replace people for some tasks, such as car assembly.
3) Continued use of computers can cause health problems, e.g. repetitive strain injury.

The Electronic Transfer of Data is Useful for Industry

The electronic transfer of data is dead useful in industry.

1) It means that design work and manufacturing work can be done in separate locations. A designer's work can be electronically transferred to the manufacturing site.
2) Electronic Data Interchange (EDI) is the direct transfer of information from one computer system to another, usually via the telephone network.
3) E-mail can be used to quickly transfer written information (and attachments) between different locations.
4) Teleconferencing allows meetings between workers in different locations. It uses a camera connected to a computer which is connected to the telephone network or Internet. Voices and moving images are relayed in real time.

The World Wide Web can be Used as a Research Tool

There's a huge amount of information on the Internet. In fact, there's so much information, it can be a right pain in the neck finding the stuff you need.

1) The simplest way to start researching information on the Internet is to use a search engine.
2) The basic type of search is a keyword search — you type in a keyword, and the search engine lists a load of websites containing that keyword.
3) You can do a more complex search using more than one keyword by linking them together with AND and OR. *(It'll assume AND if you don't use a linking word.)*
4) Alternatively, if you know the address of the web page or site you're interested in (also known as its URL — Uniform Resource Locator), you can go straight there.

ICT and when ICT I drinks it...

In the old days, when something went wrong in business (e.g. a cheque not arriving when it was supposed to), you were forced to make up a 'low-tech' excuse — maybe it had got lost in the post, for example. But nowadays, you can just say, 'The computer went down.' Much more modern.

Health and Safety

Obviously you need to watch out for yourself in the workplace — and everyone else too.

Employers have to Provide Safe Working Conditions

1) The <u>Health and Safety at Work Act</u> (1974) was passed to make sure employers provide a <u>safe working environment</u>, and that they use <u>safety signs</u> to help reduce the risk of <u>accidents</u>.
2) Factory <u>inspectors</u> are employed to <u>examine</u> and <u>investigate</u> workplaces to check that <u>rules</u> and <u>regulations</u> are being followed.
3) There is a <u>legal obligation</u> for employers and workers to ensure that they use <u>safe working practices</u> at all times.

Risk Assessments Should be Carried Out in Workplaces

1) An evaluation (called a <u>risk assessment</u>) must be carried out by an employer to <u>identify</u> and <u>minimise</u> any potential risks at work.
2) Risk assessments are especially important wherever <u>chemicals</u> or <u>machinery</u> are used.
3) Employers, workshop managers and your <u>technology teacher</u> must assess the risks involved at work or school, and put reasonable <u>precautions</u> in place to prevent accidents from happening. This might involve placing <u>warning</u> or <u>caution signs</u> on machines, installing <u>non-slip flooring</u> or putting up <u>barriers</u> and <u>guards</u>.

Safety Advice Should be Followed

A lot of this is common sense. But it's incredibly important, so pay attention...

Wear Appropriate Clothing

1) While working (especially with machine tools) make sure your <u>sleeves</u> are rolled back, <u>apron ties</u> are tucked in and if you've got <u>long hair</u>, it's tied back.
2) Protect yourself from <u>hazardous</u> materials by wearing strong protective <u>gloves</u> and <u>goggles</u>.
3) If <u>dust</u> or <u>vapours</u> are a danger, make sure there's adequate <u>ventilation</u>.
4) When <u>casting</u>, always wear <u>thick all-body suits</u>, <u>face visors</u>, <u>gauntlets</u> and <u>spats</u>.

Care Should be Taken with Tools and Machinery

1) Use the <u>safety guards</u> on lathes and drilling machines.
2) Know how to <u>switch off</u> and <u>isolate</u> machines in an emergency.
3) <u>Never</u> adjust a machine unless you've <u>switched it off</u> and isolated it <u>first</u>.
4) <u>Never</u> leave machines <u>unattended</u> while switched on.
5) Always <u>secure</u> work safely — e.g. you should clamp work securely for drilling.
6) Don't use <u>machines</u> or <u>hand tools</u> unless you have been <u>shown how</u>.
7) Ensure that any <u>dust extraction</u> equipment is connected and working properly.
8) <u>Carry</u> tools safely.

Handle Materials and Waste Sensibly

1) Make sure materials are <u>safe to handle</u>. <u>Deburr</u> metal (file down any rough edges) before you start work.
2) Beware of <u>naked flames</u> or red-hot heating elements — and keep them away from <u>flammable liquids</u>.
3) Make sure you <u>dispose of waste properly</u> (this is also an environmental issue).
4) When <u>storing</u> material, make sure it's <u>put away safely</u> so it can't fall and injure anyone.
5) Never clear away metal shavings/dust with your bare hands — <u>use the brush</u> provided.

Safe as houses — condemned houses...

Companies have to take health and safety issues very seriously these days, as workers are more willing and able to sue their employers than they were in the past. Which is nice.

Revision Summary for Section Five

So that's it then — the end of another section. The end of Section Five, in fact. And you don't get many of those. In fact, it's usually limited to one Section Five per book (unless things have gone very wrong indeed, that is). Well, you probably know what happens now then... yep, it's revision summary time. Lots of questions to check what you know, and what you don't. So keep practising them until you know all the answers. That's the best way to learn. Have a jolly time.

1) Explain the difference between good design and good manufacture.
2) Give five reasons why a consumer might choose a particular product.
3) Describe two ways a manufacturer could find out what consumers think of its product.
4) Give one reason why an evaluation is important.
5) Describe six things you could mention in your evaluation.
6) Describe five things you should think about when you're designing if you want to be socially and environmentally responsible.
7) Name three kinds of thing that can offend people if used inappropriately in a design.
8) Why are many hardwoods classed as threatened resources?
9) Explain why using a softwood is sometimes a 'greener' choice than using a hardwood.
10) Name two of the Earth's resources that are limited.
11) What happens to most waste? What problems can this cause?
12) Explain what these symbols mean: a)   b)

13) Explain why many companies register trademarks.
14) What is a patent? What kind of thing can be awarded a patent?
15) Explain why many companies like to get their products approved by an institute like the BSI or ISO. What does the CE mark signify?
16) Name six pieces of information that have to be on processed food labels.
17) Give seven advantages of using CAD.
18) Give three disadvantages of using CAD.
19) What is CAM? Give three advantages of using CAM, rather than the old-fashioned methods.
20) What does CNC stand for? Explain what this means.
21) Give four reasons why DTP packages have become popular.
22) Explain what is meant by a pixel.
23) Explain the difference between RGB and CMYK. When is each system used?
24) Give three advantages and three disadvantages of using ICT in industry.
25) Explain how you might go about trying to find information about a certain topic using the Internet.
26) What is the purpose of the Health and Safety at Work Act?
27) What is a risk assessment? Who should carry out risk assessments?
28) Give four precautions you should take when:
   a) working with machinery,   b) handling waste.

Systems and Control

Systems comprise <u>inputs</u>, <u>processes</u> (or <u>transformations</u>) and <u>outputs</u>. Like the digestive system, for example — that has an input (food), a process (turning food into energy) and an output (um...).

Systems transform *Inputs into Outputs*

① **Input** — Inputs can be anything from <u>tools</u> and <u>materials</u>, through to stuff like <u>labour</u> or <u>information</u>.

② **Process** — The <u>process</u> stage <u>transforms</u> inputs into outputs.

③ **Output** — The <u>output</u> is the <u>end product</u> of a system.

> Input devices include <u>keyboards</u>, <u>mice</u> and <u>scanners</u>.

> Processes include <u>text and image manipulation</u> (e.g. resizing, reshaping, changing colours).

> Output devices include <u>monitors</u>, <u>printers</u> and <u>speakers</u>.

Examples — *Photocopying and Printing*

Photocopying

Input: A4 original, A3 paper, toner.

Process: Image enlargement.

Output: A3 copies of the original.

Computer ink-jet/laser printing

Input: Paper, ink cartridge, print command from program.

Process: Black or four-colour process colour printing.

Output: Hard copy of design, image or artwork.

Control *and Feedback can be shown on a* Flow Chart

<u>Control</u> describes the ability to <u>change inputs</u> and so <u>alter</u> the <u>outputs</u>.
For example, you can change how dark an image is printed on a photocopier.

<u>Feedback</u> is a way of using the <u>output</u> of a system to affect the <u>input</u>.
So if you notice that a photocopier has printed something too dark, you can change the settings and make sure the next copies are lighter. On a flow chart, feedback is shown as a '<u>loop</u>':

See page 42 for more about flow charts.

This bit is the 'feedback loop'.
The decision box shows where one copy is checked, and if there's a problem, the flow chart loops back.

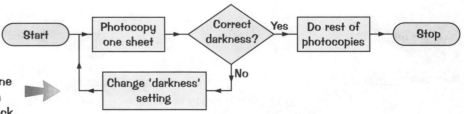

Control, control — you must learn control...

Loads of everyday tasks (like making a cup of tea, getting dressed, and so on) could be looked at as systems, and you could try to identify what their inputs, processes and outputs are. It'd be good practice, though I'm not really sure how interesting it would be. But that's life, I suppose.

Mechanisms

There are loads of simple <u>mechanisms</u> you can use. Some are better for <u>2-D items</u> (e.g. linkages in pop-up cards) and some for <u>3-D things</u> (e.g. cams in mechanical toys). But they're all <u>smashing</u>.

Mechanisms 'transfer' Motion

1) <u>Mechanisms</u> involve <u>movement</u> in a <u>rotary</u> (round and round), <u>linear</u> (along a line), <u>reciprocating</u> (back and forth along a line) or <u>oscillating</u> (swinging) motion.

2) They can <u>amplify</u> or <u>reduce</u> the size of a <u>force</u> or a <u>movement</u>.

3) They can also <u>change</u> one motion (the <u>input</u>) into another (the <u>output</u>). E.g. <u>bicycle pedals</u> move in a <u>rotary</u> motion, turning the <u>wheels</u> in a <u>rotary</u> motion, moving the bicycle in a <u>linear</u> motion.

Cams Rotate *and move a Follower*

Cams are shaped pieces of material, fixed to an <u>axle</u> or <u>shaft</u>. As they <u>rotate</u>, they make a '<u>follower</u>' move in a <u>linear</u> / <u>reciprocating</u> fashion.

There are *Three Classes* of Lever

Each class has a <u>load</u>, <u>effort</u> and <u>fulcrum</u> (or pivot point).

Load and effort on <u>different sides</u> of the <u>fulcrum</u>, e.g. scissors, crowbar.

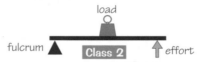

Effort <u>outside</u> the load, e.g. doors (fulcrum is the hinge), wheelbarrows (fulcrum is the wheel).

Effort <u>inside</u> the load, e.g. tweezers, elbow joint.

Linkages *can Transfer Forces*

Linkages are great for...

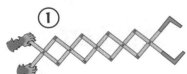

...transferring a force, e.g. lazy tongs...

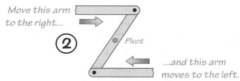

...turning a push force into a pull...

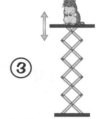

...and allowing objects to have a telescopic mechanism.

Pulleys *have Wheels and a Belt*

Pulleys are grooved wheels with a belt or rope round them.

They can <u>transfer energy</u>...

...<u>reverse the direction</u> of rotation (by putting a twist in the belt)...

...or can <u>make lifting heavy loads easier</u> (by using wheels of different sizes).

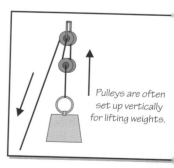

Pulleys are often set up vertically for lifting weights.

I like pulleys — they're really groove-ey...

You can make these mechanisms out of card. Make holes in the card using a bradawl (with a piece of wood underneath). And use paper fasteners or eyelets to make pivots or to join card linkages together. You'll never have as much fun again as long as you live.

Scale of Production

The term 'scale of production' is all about the <u>quantity</u> of products that you're going to manufacture. Commercially there are <u>four main categories</u> for you to learn...

Jobbing Production — Making a One-Off Product

1) This is where you're making a <u>single product</u>.
2) Every item made will be different, to meet the customer's <u>individual</u> and <u>specific requirements</u>.
3) This type of production is very <u>labour-intensive</u>, and requires a <u>highly skilled</u> workforce.
4) Examples are wide-ranging, from made-to-measure furniture to one-off buildings like the Millennium Dome.

Batch Production — A Specified Quantity of a Product

1) This is where you're making a <u>specific quantity</u> of a particular product.
2) Batches can be <u>repeated</u> as many times as required.
3) The <u>machinery</u> and <u>labour</u> used need to be <u>flexible</u>, so they can quickly change from making one batch to making another batch of a similar product.
4) The time <u>between</u> batches, when machines and tools may have to be set up differently or changed around, is called <u>down time</u>. This is <u>unproductive</u> and needs to be kept as short as possible so the manufacturer doesn't lose money.

Mass Production — High-Volume Production

1) Making products on a really <u>large scale</u>, such as cars or electrical goods.
2) Often uses <u>expensive specialised equipment</u> including computer-aided manufacturing (CAM) and industrial robots.
3) As well as all this equipment, you need a <u>large workforce</u>. The different stages of production and manufacture are <u>broken down</u> into simple <u>repetitive tasks</u> which people are able to learn easily.
4) <u>Recruitment</u> is relatively <u>easy</u> — you don't need to employ skilled people.
5) <u>In-line assembly</u> is often used for mass production.

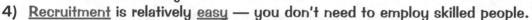

Continuous Production — Non-Stop Production 24hrs/day

1) This involves <u>non-stop</u>, uninterrupted production.
2) The specialised equipment required costs so much that it would be too <u>expensive</u> to turn it off. So it has to keep running and producing continuously.
3) Examples of continuous production include <u>oil</u> and <u>chemical</u> manufacture.

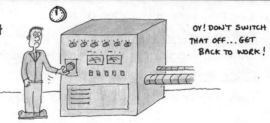

Just-in-Time Manufacturing Needs Detailed Forward Planning

1) For <u>just-in-time</u> manufacture (JIT), you only buy materials and components as and <u>when you need them</u>.
2) This removes the need for <u>large stockpiles of resources</u>, saving money and space.
3) Everything has to be kept <u>on time</u>, or things can easily go wrong.

It's not what you've got — it's how much you've got of it...

Yup, all that this lot boils down to is quantity.

Commercial Products and Packaging

It's useful to look at commercial packaging and try to work out how <u>manufacturers</u> could have made it. It could give you <u>ideas</u> for stuff that you have to make <u>yourself</u>.

Packaging for a Mobile Phone

Packaging for a <u>mobile phone</u> may comprise:

(1) a <u>die-cut carton board</u> box (see page 62),

(2) a vacuum-formed rigid <u>polystyrene</u> tray,

(3) a <u>paper</u> sleeve printed in full colour using the four process colours by <u>offset lithography</u>, and with <u>embossed</u> and <u>varnished</u> special effects to enhance the logo and photograph of the product.

A T-shirt with Packaging

A design can be <u>applied</u> to the T-shirt using the <u>screen printing</u> process or <u>iron-on vinyl</u> cut by a Roland Camm machine.

It can be <u>packaged</u> in an <u>extruded polyethylene</u> bag printed using <u>flexography</u>, and with a <u>die-cut cardboard</u> header to aid hanging.

Packaging for Milk

Milk can be packaged in a number of convenient forms:
1) in blow-moulded <u>HDPE</u> (see pages 11 and 12) containers with an injection-moulded HDPE screw cap and tamper-evident seal.
2) in <u>die-cut waxed card</u> Tetra Pak cartons.
3) in blow-moulded, reusable <u>glass</u> bottles with a <u>die-cut aluminium foil</u> seal.

Registration Marks are used by Printers

These can take a number of forms and be used for different purposes:

<u>Colour registration marks</u> are used by printers to check the <u>colour density</u> and the position or <u>alignment</u> of one colour relative to another.

They are usually square blocks or concentric circles.

<u>Crop marks</u> are used by printers to show where a printed page needs to be <u>cut to size</u> (guillotined).

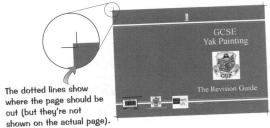

The dotted lines show where the page should be cut (but they're not shown on the actual page).

Why oh why oh why oh why oh why oh why oh why...

If you're feeling bored one day, take a number of everyday products and try to work out what they're made of and what production and printing processes were used. Then you'll be <u>really</u> bored. But if you then go back to what you were doing in the first place, it won't seem so bad.

Printing Methods

Designers and manufacturers use various <u>commercial printing methods</u>. And because I know you're desperate to know about them, I've included a whole page on them.

Letterpress uses a Flat Printing Plate

This is a form of <u>relief printing</u> — meaning the <u>image</u> or <u>type</u> (i.e. the text) is <u>raised above</u> the flat printing plate. It's used for the printing of large amounts of <u>monochrome</u> (i.e. one-colour) text — e.g. books, headed paper and business cards. Letterpress is ideal for <u>print runs</u> of 500-5000 copies, but can do fewer.

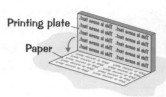

Printing plate

Paper

Flexography uses a Cylindrical Printing Plate

<u>Flexography</u> is a similar method to letterpress. However, the printing plate is made from plastic or rubber <u>cylinders</u>. It's a <u>quick</u> process and is used for large print runs, making it ideal for printing packaging, carrier bags and wallpaper.

Gravure uses an Etched Printing Plate

Gravure uses an <u>etched</u> printing plate, meaning the image is <u>lower</u> than the surface of the plate. This process is used to produce <u>quality products</u> such as magazines, books and postage stamps. It's an <u>expensive</u> process but ideal for very large print runs — half a million copies or more.

(high quality magazines)

Lithography and Offset Lithography use 'Oily' Ink

Lithography works on the principle of <u>oil</u> and <u>water</u> not mixing. An aluminium <u>printing plate</u> has a <u>relief</u> (i.e. raised) image transferred to it photographically using ultraviolet light. The plate is washed with a chemical that makes the <u>image</u> area <u>attract</u> ink, while the <u>non-image</u> area is kept <u>wet</u> (and so <u>repels</u> the 'oily' ink). Lithography's an <u>economical</u> printing process, ideal for print runs of 1000 copies and upwards — so is used to print books, posters, magazines, packaging...

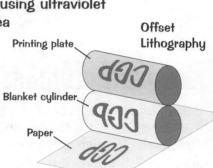

Offset Lithography

Printing plate

Blanket cylinder

Paper

In <u>offset lithography</u>, the image is first printed onto a rubber '<u>blanket</u>' cylinder, and this blanket cylinder transfers the image to the paper.

Screen Printing uses a... Screen

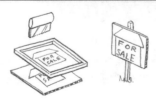

This is a <u>low-cost</u> process, and is ideal for <u>short</u> print runs (of up to a few hundred copies) where <u>fine detail</u> is not required. It's possible to print onto various <u>surfaces</u> — e.g. paper, card, fabric and corriflute (the plastic stuff they make estate agents' signs from), so is ideal for printing posters, T-shirts, wallpaper, estate agents' signs...

Flexography — for some reason that sounds like a kind of exercise...

Some people think I'm odd, but I like collecting samples (I call them swatches) of different printing methods, and labelling them to help me remember which is which. It keeps me amused for hours. Then I get my pet gerbil Eric to test me. He gives me an old button every time I get one right.

Surface Effects and Photocopiers

Special effects can be used to make graphic products look fancier. Oooh...

Die cutting is used for Cutting and Creasing

Die cutting uses a series of knives and folding/creasing bars fixed to a plywood base. These are aligned so that they cut out and crease nets (shape nets, that is — not the stringy kind) for packaging, point-of-sale displays, etc. As many nets as possible are cut out of the same sheet of card at the same time to reduce costs.

Embossing leaves a Raised Impression

Embossing means pushing a shaped die into a piece of paper or card from behind, leaving a raised impression on its surface. It's used to draw attention to a particular bit of the product, e.g. book title, logo or image. It's an expensive process but adds texture and can suggest quality.

Foil Application makes things look Fancy

(silver cross)

Foil application (or foil blocking) means 'printing' metal foil onto certain areas of a product. It's often used in packaging to draw attention to a logo, brand name, etc. Again, it's an expensive process but can give the impression of quality.

Laminating means Sandwiching in Plastic

Laminating is the process of sandwiching a document (e.g. a poster, menu or business card) between two layers of plastic. This is done by passing the document and the plastic covers through the heated rollers of a laminating machine. Many packaging materials are a lamination of different papers, cards, plastics and aluminium foil. The aim is usually to make the surface better for printing on, or to form a barrier against oxygen or moisture.

Varnishing makes things look Shiny

Varnishing is a printing effect that's added after all the other colours are printed and dry. Four types of varnish are used — oil-based, water-based, spirit-based and ultraviolet. Varnishing can be applied over the whole product or just specific areas that need highlighting — e.g. photographs and headings on packaging, catalogues or books.

Modern Photocopiers can do all kinds of Fancy Stuff

Modern photocopiers can duplicate, enlarge and reduce documents onto thin card and acetate, as well as a variety of papers. Photocopying can help in the development of a design where an outline of an object needs to be quickly and easily reproduced. Photocopiers can also collate and staple multi-page documents together.

Foil application — sounds like something Windows 98 might do...

These are all ways to make things look fancy. And this is vital, because image is everything these days. You might even be able to use some of these effects in your project, and make your idea stand out from the dross that your friends have produced. But don't tell them I said that.

Production Methods and Barcodes

Well, well, well... how times change. We didn't have <u>CAD/CAM stuff</u> in schools when I were a lad. We had to draw on bits of old Weetabix with a rat's tail dipped in melted cheese.

CAD/CAM — Computer-Aided Design / Manufacture

<u>Computer-Aided Design</u> (CAD) and Computer-Aided Manufacture (CAM) are being used more and more in the production of graphic products — both in <u>industry</u> and <u>schools</u>.

<u>CAD packages</u> work by <u>converting</u> lines, shapes and text to <u>sets of coordinates</u>. These coordinates are then <u>interpreted</u> by the <u>CAM machine</u> as lines to <u>cut out</u>, <u>plot</u> or <u>print</u>.

CAM machines can <u>cut</u>, <u>score</u> and <u>print</u> designs onto card, vinyl and other materials, making it easy to produce labels, printed T-shirts, stencils and signs.

Jigs, Templates and Moulds Improve Accuracy

Various devices can be used while making goods to <u>save time</u> and <u>improve accuracy</u>. Examples include <u>jigs</u>, <u>templates</u> and <u>moulds</u>. They're very important in <u>industry</u>.

This kind of jig fits over the end of the plank and makes it easy to drill the holes in the right places.

1) <u>Jigs</u> are used to <u>position</u> or <u>align</u> materials for drilling, sawing and so on.

2) <u>Templates</u> are things you can draw or cut around to achieve consistency of shape and size.

3) <u>Moulds</u>, <u>patterns</u> and <u>formers</u> are used to make single items, or numerous copies of something, e.g. when vacuum forming.

Scanners can Transfer Images onto a Computer

<u>Scanners</u> are used to <u>convert</u> photographs, pictures and hand-drawn images into <u>computer files</u> that can be <u>manipulated</u> using <u>graphics packages</u>. These allow the user to <u>resize</u> images, change <u>colours</u> and add various <u>effects</u>. The images produced can then be used in desktop publishing packages or word processors.

Barcodes are pretty much Everywhere nowadays

<u>Barcodes</u> are sets of vertical black and white <u>lines</u> (bars) of <u>varying thickness</u> that can be read by a <u>scanner</u> (or <u>reader</u>). The thickness of the bars and the spaces between them correspond to <u>numbers</u> that make up a unique <u>code</u> for each type of product. You see them on all kinds of goods these days, including CDs, books and food.

5 000143 057629

Hand-held and till-mounted <u>optical scanners</u> are used in some shops to read <u>barcodes</u> as goods are sold. It means that shop staff don't have to <u>remember</u> individual prices. They also make it easier to <u>record</u> sales, and to <u>control</u> stock levels and reordering. The information obtained can also be used for <u>marketing</u> purposes.

Barcodes — but why... they're dead handy...

I got a jig once. My dad bought it for me while he was away on business. He'd gone to Cork to a conference about something or other. And he brought me this jig back. Yep — it was an Irish jig.

Packaging and Waste

Packaging <u>protects</u>, <u>preserves</u> and <u>promotes</u> the product it contains
— they're called "the 3 Ps" by people in the packaging industry... maybe.

Protection — during Transit and from Customers

1) Packaging materials like cardboard and expanded polystyrene can <u>protect</u> a product from knocks and bumps during <u>transportation</u>.
2) Manufacturers can also add <u>tamper-evident seals</u> to packaging to try and prevent customers tampering with products.

Preservation — especially Foodstuffs

1) Many products (especially <u>foodstuffs</u>) begin to <u>deteriorate</u> when exposed to <u>oxygen</u> in the air.
2) Sealed <u>glass jars</u> and <u>bottles</u>, <u>'tin' cans</u> and <u>tubes</u> are traditional packages for foodstuffs, drinks and toothpaste.
3) However, <u>plastics</u> and <u>composite materials</u> (e.g. layers of card, plastic and aluminium foil laminated together) are being used more and more these days.

Promotion — to make you Buy More Stuff

1) Manufacturers often use striking <u>colours</u> and <u>shapes</u> of packaging to <u>entice</u> you to <u>buy</u> their products.
2) As well as the names of the <u>manufacturer</u> and the <u>product</u>, the packaging may include pictures or images showing <u>how</u> the product should be <u>used</u>, or a <u>contact address</u> (or anything else for that matter).
3) It may also include a '<u>flash</u>' showing <u>money off</u> or a catchy <u>slogan</u>, e.g. '*CGP — Buy our chickens, they're ace*'.

Avoid Unnecessary Waste with the 3 Rs

<u>Unnecessary</u> and <u>waste</u> packaging is a big problem.
But there are things the <u>public</u> and <u>industry</u> can do to help.

Reduction — use materials <u>economically</u> by using designs that <u>tessellate</u> (which will produce less waste). It's also a smart idea to <u>avoid</u> unnecessary packaging, e.g. by selling chocolates in a <u>paper bag</u> rather than a plastic tray in a cardboard box wrapped in cellophane.

Reusing — milk bottles, jam jars and egg boxes can be <u>reused</u> many times.

Recycling — recycling materials (e.g. card, glass, plastic, metal) means they can be used again to make the <u>same</u> or <u>different</u> products.

> "The only 'bad' packaging from an environmental viewpoint is at the extremes — under-packaging is disastrous, over-packaging is deplorable, and deceptive packaging is illegal." (The Institute of Packaging)

Avoid unnecessary waste — eat this book once you've read it...

I went into a shop the other day and saw a yoghurt in the fridge that had a tamper-evident seal. Anyway, I picked the yoghurt up and must have handled it a bit roughly, because the seal started barking and banging its flippers together. It gave me a right fright. And I had to buy the yoghurt.

Revision Summary

That section was a thing of rare wonder and beauty, I'm sure you'll agree. And what could be more smashing now than to make sure you've really learnt what was in it... Well, as luck would have it, I have some particularly lovely questions here to help you do just that. Yes, I know... that was <u>very</u> thoughtful of me, wasn't it. But you know, I just couldn't stand the thought of you standing there like Oliver Twist looking all upset and asking for more. I had to do something about it — and that's why I wrote these. Just make sure you can answer all of them without any problem whatsoever, and then you can call it a day.

1) What are the three things that make up a system?

2) Name two computer input devices and two computer output devices.

3) What is 'control' in a system?

4) Describe how feedback works. How is feedback shown on a flow chart?

5) Name four kinds of mechanism.

6) Describe the three classes of lever.

7) Describe three uses of: a) linkages, and b) pulleys.

8) List the four main scales of production.

9) Explain what 'just-in-time production' is.

10) What are crop marks used for? And registration marks?

11) Explain the difference between letterpress printing and flexography.

12) Explain briefly how lithography and offset lithography work.

13) Name three surfaces you can use screen printing on.

14) Describe the following:
a) die cutting, b) embossing, c) laminating, d) varnishing.

15) Apart from copying an image, name three other functions a photocopier can perform.

16) Explain what is meant by CAD/CAM.

17) How can jigs improve accuracy in manufacturing?

18) Name two advantages of using barcodes.

19) Describe the three purposes of packaging.

20) Explain three ways in which waste can be limited.

Tips on Getting Started

This section's got all the stuff people don't do that the exam boards get really annoyed about.
Read this before you start your project to make sure you keep those markers happy.

Step 1 — Get your Idea

You can get ideas from different places — for example, your teacher might:

1) tell you exactly what your task is.

2) give you a range of tasks to choose from.

3) leave the project choice completely up to you.

Don't choose anything Too Easy or Too Boring

Choose a project that will:

1) stretch you and let you demonstrate just how good you are. If the project's too easy, or contains little scope for design, then you'll lose valuable marks.

2) be interesting and challenging enough to keep you motivated. Coursework's a long old process, and you need to stay committed.

3) give you the opportunity to produce a wide range of research, and demonstrate your ICT skills.

4) allow for a variety of solutions, resulting in a project which can be completed before the deadline (and this includes allowing time for testing and evaluation).

The Design Brief — Give Loads of Detail

See page 1 for more on the design brief.

1) Your idea needs to have "real commercial potential".

2) You need to describe exactly what you're trying to do.

3) Explain all the factors you need to consider — things like price, weight, market trends, etc.

Say Why your Research is Relevant

1) DON'T just plonk bits of paper in your research folder without any explanation.

2) DON'T just copy and paste stuff from the Internet either.

3) DO write notes on every piece of research to say why it's relevant, how it changed your thinking or how it backed up your existing ideas.

4) DO refer back to the research section throughout the project — that helps to show you've used your research.

See page 2 for more on research.

THIS IS ALL YOU NEED TO DO:

Print or photocopy the relevant stuff. →

> This is my groovy research that I got off the Internet. This is my groovy research that I got off the Internet. This is my groovy research that I got off the Internet. This is my groovy research that I got off the Internet. This is my groovy research that I got off the Internet. This is my groovy research that I got off the Internet. This is my groovy research that I got off the Internet. This is my groovy research that I got off the Internet.

Highlight the really useful bits. →

Write brief notes saying where you found it... →

> I found this on Bob's Groovy Tennis Ball Website (www.bobsballs.co.uk).

...what you found out... →

> The highlighted part explains how the fluorescent yellow fur affects the aerodynamics of the ball. I hadn't previously considered the effect this could have, so I will now factor

...and what effect it's had on your project. →

> the use of different materials into my testing.

Remember — your research analysis will contain all the conclusions from research. But these notes will help you write that research analysis, and will also help the examiner understand why you made your decisions.

Tips on Development

If you're smart you'll keep planning and evaluating throughout your project. If you're a buffoon you'll do a bit at the start, then forget about it and get a bad mark for your project.

You Need a Wide Range of Ideas — Be Creative

1) There's more than one way to skin a cat.

2) Consider plenty of different ways to solve the problem.

3) Don't just come up with one good idea and stick with it.
You'll only be sure it's the best idea if you've thought about other ways of doing it.

4) The examiners do really get annoyed about this one —
so get those creative juices flowing.

Developing your Ideas — Try Out a Few Alternatives

1) The same goes for developing ideas as for creating them.

2) There's still more than one way to skin a cat.

3) Once you've got the idea, there are still plenty of ways to turn that into an ace product.

Do Loads of Planning — and Not Just at the Start

Planning is for life, not just for... um... the start of your project.
These are the things you should do:

OVERALL PROJECT PLAN AT THE START:

1) to help you focus on the task

2) to make sure you know what stage you should have reached at
any time — this way, if you fall behind schedule, you'll know
about it as soon as possible, and can do something about it

3) to allow enough time for all the different stages of the design
process — including testing, evaluation, and writing up your project

Remember to include testing and evaluating in your time plan — it's all too easy to forget them...

PLAN YOUR RESEARCH:

Work out what research you need to do, and how long you're going to allow yourself
for each bit (e.g. questionnaires, disassembling a competing product, and so on).

DON'T GET BOGGED DOWN:

When you're generating proposals or developing your product, don't spend too long
working on one little aspect of the product. There's a lot to do — so try to keep your
project moving forward.

I have a cunning plan...

OK, repeat after me: "I will allow time for testing in my time plan. I will allow time for testing in my
time plan. I will allow time for testing in my time plan. I will allow time for testing in my time plan..."

Tips on Evaluation

<u>Evaluation</u> means <u>examining</u> and <u>judging</u> your work (and <u>you</u> have to do this as part of your project — it's not just something for the examiner to do). If your product doesn't work, but you explain <u>why</u>, you can still get <u>good marks</u>.

Test and Evaluate your Product Throughout the Project

I quote:

> *"To be achieving the highest marks in this section, candidates must show that they have used a clear and objective testing strategy."*

That's from one of the Chief Examiners' Reports.
(In other words, it's important.)

Don't Wait until you're Finished to Evaluate your Work

1)   Like any designer, it's a good idea to be thinking about <u>evaluation</u> from the moment you <u>start</u> working on your <u>design brief</u>.

2)   Make <u>notes</u> on your <u>designs</u> and <u>developments</u> as you go along, explaining what was <u>good</u> and <u>bad</u> about each one.

3)   When you're writing up your <u>final evaluation</u>, you can also think about whether you'd do anything <u>differently</u> if you were starting again. It's okay if you made some <u>bad decisions</u> during your project — everyone does. But you can get marks if you <u>explain why</u> they were bad decisions, and what you <u>wish</u> you'd done instead.

Check your Brief and Specification

You need to evaluate your product <u>fully</u>. Use these guidelines:

1)   <u>Compare</u> your final product to your <u>brief</u> and <u>specification</u>. Does your product satisfy all the conditions it's supposed to? If not, why not?

2)   Try to get a <u>likely user</u> (or an expert in this kind of product, maybe) to <u>trial</u> your product and give their <u>honest opinions</u>. This will give you a <u>realistic view</u> of whether it's <u>fit for its purpose</u> — e.g. does it do what it's meant to? And if it does, how well? They may also be able to give you ideas for improvements.

3)   It's also dead important to think about things you could have done better, such as...

① <u>Time implications</u> — did you spend too much time in one area, or rush to finish?

② <u>Practical work</u> — were you completely <u>satisfied</u> with the <u>quality</u> of your final product?

③ Would you <u>approach</u> aspects of your design and development work in a <u>different</u> way?

Never forget to check your briefs...

Everyone makes mistakes (well, everyone except me, obviously). More specifically, everyone makes mistakes in their D & T projects. So don't worry too much when it happens to you.
Just explain what went wrong and how you'd avoid it in the future. You can get marks for that.

Tips on Presentation

It's no use doing a stonking project if your presentation's naff. You've put a lot of time and effort into your project (probably) so it would be a shame for you to mess it up at the last stage.

IT REALLY IS WORTH PUTTING IN THOSE FEW EXTRA HOURS.

The Finished Product — Good Photographs are Ace

Your evaluation should be <u>clearly presented</u> and <u>easy to read</u>.

1) Include an introduction to give a bit of <u>background information</u> — e.g. how you came to think of the project.

2) Always take photos of any <u>non-permanent</u> work or <u>intermediate stages</u> in making the product. You can use either a <u>normal</u> or a <u>digital camera</u> and then either <u>glue in</u> the print or <u>place</u> the digital image into a word-processed document — whatever suits.

> Photos are the only way of getting a lasting record of your work — and the examiners *REALLY WANT* you to do it.

3) Use a <u>mixture of media</u> to present your project. It's always good to <u>show off</u> how nifty you are with CAD or that desktop publishing program, but don't forget about <u>old-fashioned words</u> to explain what you did, and <u>sketches</u> and <u>prototypes</u> to show how you did it.

4) Split up your evaluation into <u>different sections</u> to make it easy to read. Give each section a <u>clear heading</u>.

The sections could include:
a) how well your product satisfies the brief and specification
b) results from user trials
c) problems you encountered
d) improvements for the future

5) Think about how it fits together — your project needs to work <u>*as a whole*</u>. It should flow <u>seamlessly</u> from one bit to the next — don't just shove loads of separate bits in with no clue as to how they fit together.

Vocabulary — use the Right Technical Terms

BIG, FANCY WORDS:
1) Do yourself a favour — <u>learn all the technical terms</u>.
2) And how to <u>spell</u> them.
3) And don't worry if you sound <u>poncy</u>.
4) Using the right technical terms <u>impresses the examiners</u>. They say so in their reports.

GRAMMAR, SPELLING, PUNCTUATION:
1) Treat your project like an <u>English essay</u>.
2) Get your <u>spellings</u> right. Double-check any words you often get wrong.
3) Remember to use full stops and capital letters and write in <u>proper sentences</u>.
4) <u>Short sentences</u> make your work clearer. Long sentences, with loads of commas, can often get very confusing, because it's easy, once you get to the end of the sentence, to forget what you were reading right at the start.
5) Structure your work in <u>paragraphs</u> — a new paragraph for a new topic.

Santa cheats at presentation — he uses elves...

Of course your project has to look nice. I mean, what would you rather read... a beautifully presented folder of work, or something scribbled down on the back of a mucky paper towel...

Section Seven — Project Advice

Summary Checklist

This stuff can really make your project _sparkle_.
That's why I've given it a whole extra page — so you can't forget <u>any</u> of it.

Before you hand in your project, make sure you've covered all of these bits,
and you'll be well on your way to D & T heaven. ☺

Sparkly Project Checklist

☐ 1) My design brief has loads of detail.

☐ 2) I've done plenty of research, and said why it's relevant.

☐ 3) I've made a detailed design specification.

☐ 4) I've come up with a wide range of project proposals.

☐ 5) I've included different ways of developing my product, and explained why I made my decisions.

☐ 6) I've tested my product on consumers.

7) I've done loads of planning, including:

☐   a) a production plan (time plan),

☐   b) planning for mass production.

☐ 8) I've evaluated my product throughout the project.

☐ 9) I've taken photos of intermediate stages and anything that won't last.

☐ 10) I've used a mixture of media to present my project.

☐ 11) I've checked my spelling and grammar.

☐ 12) I've used the right technical terms.

Ultimate Frisbee

This page is an introduction to the beautiful world of Ultimate Frisbee.
Once you've finished your exams, this is an ideal way to spend those long summer months.

Each Team Starts Within its Endzone

1) The field is split into three parts —
each team's endzone and the central area.

2) There are seven players on each team. The game
starts with each team standing on the edge of their
own endzone. One team throws the disc towards
the other team (this is called a "pull").

3) The attacking team then pick up the disc
and pass it between team members.

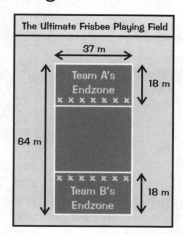

The Ultimate Frisbee Playing Field

37 m

Team A's
Endzone
× × × × × × ×

18 m

64 m

× × × × × × ×
Team B's
Endzone

18 m

Ultimate Frisbee is Played a bit like Rugby...

1) You score a point if you pass the disc to one of your
team members within the opposite endzone.

2) If the attacking team drops the disc then the defending
team take possession and become the attackers.

3) The defending team can also gain possession by
knocking the disc out of the air.

4) When you have possession of the disc, you've got 10
seconds to throw it away again. The defender marking
the player with the disc counts out to 10.

5) You can pass the disc in any direction, but you can't run
with the disc.

6) Substitutions can be made after any point is scored.

Frisbee Facts:

- The frisbee was invented
when workers at the Frisbie
Pie Company in Connecticut
started lobbing pie trays
around when they were bored.

- It's possible to pour three
whole pints of milk into a
regulation size frisbee.

- The first frisbees were sold in
the 1950s under the name
"Wham-O Pluto Platters".

... but it's a Non-Contact Sport

1) No physical contact is allowed between players
— if there is contact a foul occurs.
The fouled player carries on with possession of
the disc.

2) Ultimate frisbee has no referee. Every player is
responsible for their own foul calls...

3) ...which means that everyone has to be a
pretty good sport about it all.

Dogs are not allowed
to play Ultimate.

Just don't revise this stuff instead of Graphic Products...

Ultimate Frisbee is my new favourite sport. It's ace — we play it every Monday. I know you've
had a hard time, doing projects and revising... so I thought I'd share the gift of frisbee with you.

Index

Index